ORIGO
STEPPING STONES
2.0
COMPREHENSIVE MATHEMATICS

AUTHORS

James Burnett
Calvin Irons
Peter Stowasser
Allan Turton

PROGRAM CONSULTANTS

Diana Lambdin
Frank Lester, Jr.
Kit Norris

CONTRIBUTING WRITERS

Debi DePaul
Beth Lewis

STUDENT BOOK B

ORIGO
EDUCATION

CONTENTS

ORIGO Stepping Stones • Grade 5

CONTENTS

© ORIGO Education

Step In

A dressmaker ordered some ribbon.

About how much longer is the white ribbon than the pink ribbon?

How would you use the number line to calculate the exact difference?

Order Form

Ribbon (white)	$2\frac{1}{4}$ yards
Ribbon (pink)	$\frac{3}{4}$ yard
Ribbon (laced)	$4\frac{3}{4}$ yards

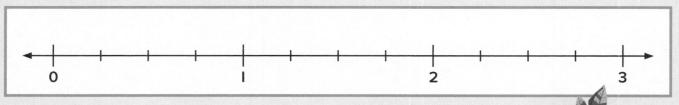

> I would mark the length of each ribbon, then count by fourths from the shorter length to the longer length to figure out the difference.

How would you calculate the difference between the lengths of the laced ribbon and the white ribbon?

Describe each of these strategies.

Which strategy do you prefer? Why?

$$4\frac{3}{4} - 2\frac{1}{4}$$
$$4 - 2 = 2$$
$$\frac{3}{4} - \frac{1}{4} = \frac{2}{4}$$
So $2 + \frac{2}{4} = 2\frac{2}{4}$

$$4\frac{3}{4} - 2\frac{1}{4}$$
is equivalent to
$$\frac{19}{4} - \frac{9}{4}$$
$$\frac{19}{4} - \frac{9}{4} = \frac{10}{4} = 2\frac{1}{2}$$

When you subtract fractions with the same denominator, what part of the answer stays the same? What part of the answer changes?

Step Up

1. Complete each equation. Use the number line to help.

a.
$$\frac{8}{6} - \frac{3}{6} = \underline{}$$

b.
$$2\frac{2}{6} - 1\frac{5}{6} = \underline{}$$

c.
$$1\frac{5}{6} - \frac{7}{6} = \underline{}$$

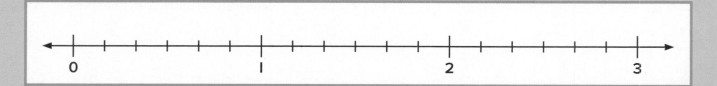

2. Complete each equation. Rewrite the fractions or mixed numbers, if necessary, to help calculate the difference.

a.

$$\frac{4}{5} - \frac{1}{5} = \boxed{}$$

b.

$$\frac{10}{3} - \frac{4}{3} = \boxed{}$$

c.

$$\frac{11}{8} - \frac{9}{8} = \boxed{}$$

d.

$$2\frac{3}{4} - \frac{1}{4} = \boxed{}$$

e.

$$3\frac{2}{5} - \frac{7}{5} = \boxed{}$$

f.

$$\frac{21}{10} - 1\frac{5}{10} = \boxed{}$$

g.

$$3\frac{2}{3} - 1\frac{1}{3} = \boxed{}$$

h.

$$4\frac{6}{10} - 3\frac{5}{10} = \boxed{}$$

i.

$$3\frac{1}{8} - 2\frac{3}{8} = \boxed{}$$

Step Ahead   Complete three different equations that show the same difference.

a.

$$\boxed{} - \boxed{} = \frac{4}{5}$$

b.

$$\boxed{} - \boxed{} = \frac{4}{5}$$

c.

$$\boxed{} - \boxed{} = \frac{4}{5}$$

© ORIGO Education

Step In These pizzas were left over after a party.

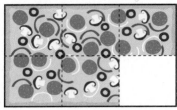
Super Supreme

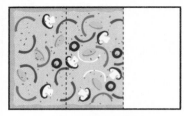
Very Veggie

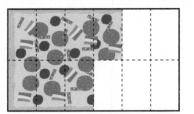
Mostly Meat

Which pizza had the most left over? How do you know?

What do you notice about each pair of fractions shown below?

How do they match the pictures of the pizzas?

$$\frac{2}{3} - \frac{7}{12} = \underline{\qquad}$$

$$\frac{5}{6} - \frac{2}{3} = \underline{\qquad}$$

$$\frac{5}{12} - \frac{1}{3} = \underline{\qquad}$$

What must you do to calculate each difference?

How could you use this diagram to help calculate $\frac{2}{3} - \frac{7}{12}$?

Complete the equation below to find the difference.

$$\underline{\qquad} - \frac{7}{12} = \underline{\qquad}$$

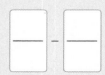

What other differences can you calculate?

Step Up 1. Rewrite each fraction to calculate the difference. Use the diagram to help. Then write the difference.

a.
$$\frac{4}{5} - \frac{7}{10} = \underline{\qquad}$$

$$\underline{\qquad} - \underline{\qquad}$$

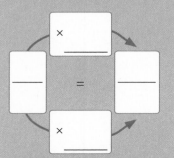

b.
$$\frac{2}{3} - \frac{2}{9} = \underline{\qquad}$$

$$\underline{\qquad} - \underline{\qquad}$$

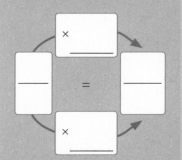

2. Write the fractions so the denominators are the same. Complete each equation.

a.
$$\frac{2}{3} - \frac{5}{9} = \underline{\qquad}$$

b.
$$\frac{5}{8} - \frac{7}{16} = \underline{\qquad}$$

c.
$$\frac{11}{15} - \frac{2}{5} = \underline{\qquad}$$

d.
$$\frac{15}{16} - \frac{3}{4} = \underline{\qquad}$$

e.
$$\frac{5}{20} - \frac{1}{4} = \underline{\qquad}$$

f.
$$\frac{19}{24} - \frac{2}{3} = \underline{\qquad}$$

3. Solve each problem. Show your thinking.

a. Henry bought a pet beetle. After a few weeks it had grown an extra $\frac{1}{4}$ of an inch. It is now $\frac{7}{8}$ of an inch long. How long was the beetle when Henry first bought it?

 in

b. A cake is cut into 16 slices. After 5 minutes 7 slices are left. After 2 minutes more, $\frac{1}{4}$ of the cake is left. How many slices were eaten in those 2 minutes?

_____ slices

Step Ahead   Complete each equation. Use denominators that are different from the denominator of the fraction answer. The first one has been done for you.

$$\frac{1}{2} = \frac{3}{4} - \frac{1}{4}$$

$$\frac{5}{6} = \underline{\qquad} - \underline{\qquad}$$

$$\frac{2}{3} = \underline{\qquad} - \underline{\qquad}$$

$$\frac{6}{7} = \underline{\qquad} - \underline{\qquad}$$

$$\frac{3}{4} = \underline{\qquad} - \underline{\qquad}$$

$$\frac{7}{8} = \underline{\qquad} - \underline{\qquad}$$

$$\frac{4}{5} = \underline{\qquad} - \underline{\qquad}$$

$$\frac{8}{9} = \underline{\qquad} - \underline{\qquad}$$

Computation Practice

What is the difference between *here* and *there*?

★ Complete the equations. Then find each product in the puzzle below and shade the matching letter. The remaining letters spell the answer.

3 × 260 = _____	140 × 5 = _____	170 × 3 = _____
4 × 180 = _____	3 × 160 = _____	190 × 5 = _____
280 × 3 = _____	240 × 4 = _____	3 × 310 = _____
250 × 3 = _____	3 × 130 = _____	160 × 4 = _____
180 × 5 = _____	190 × 4 = _____	5 × 130 = _____
140 × 3 = _____	3 × 290 = _____	230 × 4 = _____
3 × 180 = _____		

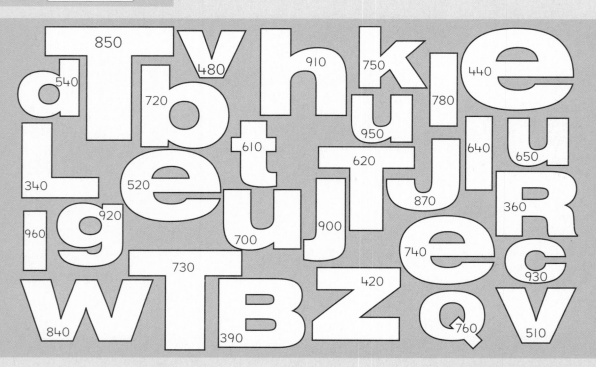

© ORIGO Education

Ongoing Practice

1. Draw jumps on the number line to calculate each difference.

a.

$8.7 - 3.4 =$ _____

⟵———————————————————————⟶

b.

$6.4 - 3.2 =$ _____

⟵———————————————————————⟶

c.

$7.6 - 5.3 =$ _____

⟵———————————————————————⟶

FROM 5.5.5

2. Complete each equation. Rewrite the fractions so the denominators are the same.

a.

$$\frac{3}{5} - \frac{4}{10} = \underline{\quad}$$

b.

$$\frac{17}{20} - \frac{5}{10} = \underline{\quad}$$

c.

$$\frac{8}{10} - \frac{3}{5} = \underline{\quad}$$

FROM 5.7.2

Preparing for Module 8

Each large shape is one whole.
Shade each shape to match the equation, then write the product.

a.

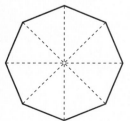

$3 \times \dfrac{2}{8} =$ ☐

b.

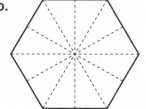

$2 \times \dfrac{3}{12} =$ ☐

c.

$2 \times \dfrac{2}{6} =$ ☐

d.

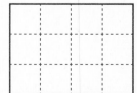

$4 \times \dfrac{2}{12} =$ ☐

Step In

Each of these pitchers holds 1 quart.

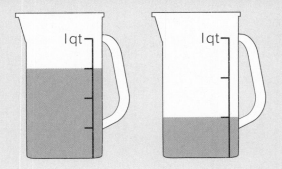

How much water is in each pitcher?

How would you calculate the difference between
the amount of water in each pitcher?

> I will need to rewrite both fractions
> so the denominators are the same.

What denominator do the two fractions have
in common?

Use these diagrams to find two equivalent
fractions that share a common denominator.

Complete the equation below to calculate
the difference.

$$\frac{}{12} - \frac{}{12} = \frac{}{12}$$

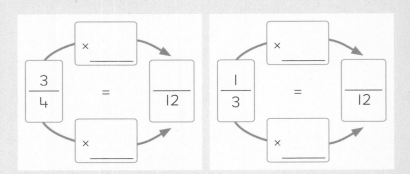

Step Up

1. Use the diagram to find equivalent fractions that share a common
denominator. Rewrite the fractions. Then write the difference.

a.

$$\frac{4}{5} - \frac{1}{3} = \frac{}{}$$

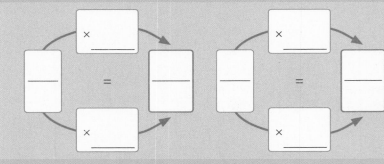

b.

$$\frac{1}{2} - \frac{1}{5} = \frac{}{}$$

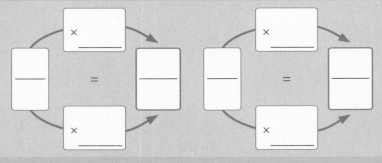

2. Estimate the difference then rewrite **both** fractions so the denominators are the same. Complete each equation.

a.
$$\frac{1}{3} - \frac{1}{4} = \underline{\hspace{1cm}}$$

b.
$$\frac{2}{5} - \frac{1}{6} = \underline{\hspace{1cm}}$$

c.
$$\frac{3}{4} - \frac{1}{6} = \underline{\hspace{1cm}}$$

d.
$$\frac{3}{7} - \frac{1}{4} = \underline{\hspace{1cm}}$$

e.
$$\frac{5}{8} - \frac{1}{3} = \underline{\hspace{1cm}}$$

f.
$$\frac{7}{12} - \frac{3}{8} = \underline{\hspace{1cm}}$$

3. Solve each problem. Show your thinking.

a. Three-fifths of a field is planted with potatoes. Another section of the field is planted with garlic. Eleven-twelfths of the field is planted in total. What fraction of the field is planted with garlic?

b. In a park, $\frac{5}{8}$ of the animals are pigeons and $\frac{2}{10}$ of the animals are squirrels. What fraction of all the animals in the park are not pigeons or squirrels?

Step Ahead

Hannah bakes an apple pie. She gives one-third of the pie to her friend. She gives one-fourth of the pie to her son. She puts the rest in the fridge. What fraction of the pie did she put in the fridge? Show your thinking.

Step In

Mika bought these two strips of wood to make a picture frame.

$5\frac{1}{4}$ feet

$7\frac{1}{2}$ feet

How could you calculate the difference in length?

Look at these students' methods.

Megan subtracted using improper fractions.	Andrea subtracted the whole numbers and then subtracted the fractions.

$$\frac{15}{2} - \frac{21}{4} = \underline{\qquad}$$

$$7 - 5 = \boxed{} \qquad \frac{1}{2} - \frac{1}{4} = \dfrac{\boxed{}}{}$$

$$\boxed{} + \dfrac{\boxed{}}{} = \boxed{}$$

The denominators are related, so they only have to change one of them.

Before they subtract, what will they need to do with the fractions?

What steps will each student follow to calculate the difference?

Step Up

I. Calculate each difference using improper fractions. Show your thinking.

a.

$$3\frac{3}{4} - 1\frac{5}{8} = \boxed{}$$

b.

$$4\frac{1}{3} - 2\frac{1}{6} = \boxed{}$$

2. Calculate each difference using mixed numbers. Show your thinking.

a.

$$2 \frac{7}{12} - 2 \frac{1}{4} = \boxed{}$$

b.

$$3 \frac{9}{10} - 2 \frac{3}{5} = \boxed{}$$

3. Look at this picture frame.

a. How much longer is the longer side than the shorter side?

$\boxed{}$ ft

$3 \frac{3}{8}$ ft

$2 \frac{1}{4}$ ft

b. Imagine the two labeled lengths are cut from a strip of wood that is $7 \frac{3}{4}$ feet long. How much of the strip would be left over?

$\boxed{}$ ft

Step Ahead

What is the widest rectangular picture frame you could make using these two strips of wood? Draw a picture of the frame to show your thinking. Make sure you label the dimensions.

$6 \frac{1}{2}$ feet

$5 \frac{3}{4}$ feet

Think and Solve

Write the numbers on the sign in the grid to match the clues below.

Clues

All numbers in a row must have a common factor greater than 1.

All numbers in a column must have a common factor greater than 1.

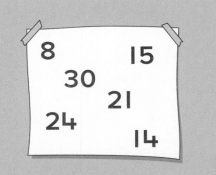

Words at Work

Write in words how you solve this problem.
There is more than one possible solution.

Deon bought a bag of apples that weighed more than 3 kilograms but less than 4 kilograms. Monique bought a bag of apples that weighed $\frac{7}{8}$ of a kilogram less than Deon's bag of apples. Hunter bought the same amount of apples as Deon and Monique together. What could be the mass of the apples each person bought?

Ongoing Practice

1. Use a written method to calculate the difference between each pair of weights.

a.

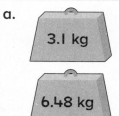

3.1 kg

6.48 kg

☐ _____ kg

b.

8.59 kg

4.05 kg

☐ _____ kg

c.

9.06 kg

12.3 kg

☐ _____ kg

d.

4.5 kg

15.81 kg

☐ _____ kg

2. Complete each equation. Show your thinking.

a. $\dfrac{2}{3} - \dfrac{3}{5} = \boxed{}$

b. $\boxed{} - \dfrac{1}{6} = \boxed{}$

c. $\dfrac{4}{5} - \dfrac{2}{4} = \boxed{}$

Preparing for Module 8

Complete the division facts.

a. $42 \div \boxed{} = 7$

b. $54 \div \boxed{} = 9$

c. $64 \div 8 = \boxed{}$

d. $\boxed{} \div 7 = 7$

e. $\boxed{} \div 3 = 9$

f. $48 \div 8 = \boxed{}$

g. $72 \div 9 = \boxed{}$

h. $56 \div \boxed{} = 8$

i. $\boxed{} \div 9 = 5$

j. $63 \div \boxed{} = 9$

k. $60 \div 10 = \boxed{}$

l. $\boxed{} \div 7 = 5$

Step In

How could you calculate the difference between the amounts of apple juice and pineapple juice in this recipe?

Fruit Punch

$1 \frac{2}{3}$ cups apple juice

$2 \frac{3}{4}$ cups pineapple juice

$2 \frac{1}{3}$ cups cranberry juice

$3 \frac{1}{2}$ cups soda water

Carter changed the amounts to improper fractions to subtract.

$$\frac{11}{4} - \frac{5}{3} = \underline{}$$

Abigail used mixed numbers.

$$2 \frac{3}{4} - 1 \frac{2}{3} = \boxed{}$$

What will Carter and Abigail need to do before they can subtract?

How should Carter rewrite the fractions to subtract?
What steps could he follow to calculate the difference?

How should Abigail rewrite the fractions to subtract?
What steps could she follow to calculate the difference?

What different ways could Abigail calculate the difference?

How could you check that Carter's answer and Abigail's answer are equal?

Step Up

1. Calculate each difference using improper fractions. Show your thinking.

a.

$$3 \frac{1}{3} - 1 \frac{1}{4} = \underline{}$$

b.

$$2 \frac{4}{6} - 1 \frac{2}{5} = \underline{}$$

2. Calculate each difference using mixed numbers. Show your thinking.

a.

$$2\frac{3}{5} - 1\frac{1}{4} = \boxed{}$$

b.

$$3\frac{3}{4} - 1\frac{1}{7} = \boxed{}$$

3. Use the recipe at the top of page 256. Solve each problem. Show your thinking.

a. How much more soda water than cranberry juice is used for the recipe?

$\boxed{}$ cups

b. Cole only has $\frac{1}{4}$ cup of apple juice. How much more apple juice does he need for this recipe?

$\boxed{}$ cups

Step Ahead

Look at the recipe at the top of page 256. How much more fruit juice is used in the recipe than soda water? Show your thinking.

 cups

Step In	How could you calculate the difference between the amounts in these two pots?

$1\frac{1}{2}$ qt

$3\frac{1}{3}$ qt

Why is it necessary to rewrite the fractions?

$$3\frac{1}{3} - 1\frac{1}{2} = 3\frac{2}{6} - 1\frac{3}{6} = \boxed{}$$

I'll have to write $3\frac{2}{6}$ in a different way to solve the problem.

$3\frac{2}{6} = 1 + 1 + \frac{8}{6}$, or $2\frac{8}{6}$

Try to subtract the fractions first.
What do you notice?

Jack and Naomi share their strategies.

Jack wrote the mixed numbers as improper fractions to make it easier to subtract.

$$3\frac{1}{3} - 1\frac{1}{2}$$

$$3\frac{2}{6} - 1\frac{3}{6}$$

$$\frac{\boxed{}}{6} - \frac{\boxed{}}{6} = \boxed{}$$

What steps do you think he used?
Write the missing values in his equation.

Naomi worked with the mixed numbers.

$$3\frac{1}{3} - 1\frac{1}{2}$$

$$3\frac{2}{6} - 1\frac{3}{6}$$

$$2\frac{8}{6} - 1\frac{3}{6} = \boxed{}$$

What steps do you think she used?
Why did she write $2\frac{8}{6}$ to help subtract?
Write the missing value in her equation.

How could you check that Naomi's answer and Jack's answer are equal?

Step Up	1. For each of these equations, rewrite the mixed numbers so the fractions have the same denominators. Show how you subtract to find the difference.

a.

$$3\frac{1}{2} - 1\frac{4}{6} = \boxed{}$$

b.

$$2\frac{3}{4} - 1\frac{5}{6} = \boxed{}$$

2. Estimate, then calculate each difference. Show your thinking.

a.

$$2\tfrac{1}{4} - 1\tfrac{1}{3} = \boxed{}$$

b.

$$2\tfrac{2}{3} - 1\tfrac{9}{15} = \boxed{}$$

3. This is another way to subtract mixed numbers. First, change both numbers to improper fractions. Then find a common denominator.

$$3\tfrac{1}{3} - 1\tfrac{1}{2} = \tfrac{10}{3} - \tfrac{3}{2} = \frac{\boxed{}}{6} - \frac{\boxed{}}{6} = \boxed{}$$

Use the same steps to calculate these differences.

	Change to improper fractions	Same denominators and subtract
a. $2\tfrac{1}{4} - 1\tfrac{3}{5}$		
b. $3\tfrac{1}{4} - 1\tfrac{2}{3}$		

Step Ahead

Complete the equation. Then explain the steps that you followed to solve it.

$$3\tfrac{1}{3} - 1\tfrac{4}{5} = \boxed{}$$

Computation Practice

What was more useful than the invention of the first telephone?

★ Complete the equations. Then write each letter above its matching total at the bottom of the page.

55¢ + $3.95 + $4.40 = $_____ **e**

$4.05 + $1.60 + 30¢ = $_____ **t**

$2.50 + 25¢ + $3.15 = $_____ **l**

$2.15 + $3.20 + $1.30 = $_____ **h**

$4.35 + $2.20 + $3.20 = $_____ **c**

$7.45 + $1.05 + $1.35 = $_____ **o**

$5.10 + $1.35 + $2.25 = $_____ **n**

$4.25 + $1.40 + $2.25 = $_____ **e**

$3.05 + $2.30 + $1.15 = $_____ **e**

$7.25 + 35¢ + 20¢ = $_____ **e**

35¢ + $2.50 + $4.05 = $_____ **p**

$3.45 + $1.40 + 10¢ = $_____ **t**

35¢ + $1.60 + $2.00 = $_____ **n**

$2.30 + $1.15 + $1.45 = $_____ **o**

$2.10 + $3.55 + $1.15 = $_____ **e**

$3.15 + $2.20 + $3.45 = $_____ **d**

$3.20 + $2.30 + $3.35 = $_____ **s**

$1.65 + $4.05 + $2.00 = $_____ **h**

$4.95	$6.65	$8.90		$8.85	$7.90	$9.75	$4.90	$8.70	$8.80

$5.95	$6.50	$5.90	$7.80	$6.90	$7.70	$9.85	$3.95	$6.80

Ongoing Practice

1. Estimate, then use the standard algorithm to calculate each difference.

a.	24.6 − 19.8	b.	18.05 − 7.12	c.	15.3 − 12.85

2. Estimate then calculate each difference using improper fractions. Show your thinking.

a.

$3\frac{7}{8} - 1\frac{3}{4} = \boxed{}$

b.

$4\frac{4}{6} - 2\frac{1}{3} = \boxed{}$

Preparing for Module 8

For each number line, the distance from 0 to 1 is one whole. Solve each problem. Draw jumps on the number line to show your thinking.

a. One batch of granola bars required $\frac{1}{6}$ of a cup of nuts. Carrina uses $\frac{5}{6}$ of a cup of nuts. How many batches of granola bars does she make?

$\boxed{}$

b. A pie is cut into eighths. After Isaac and his friends eat some pieces of pie, there are $\frac{2}{8}$ left over. How many pieces of pie did Isaac and his friends eat?

$\boxed{}$

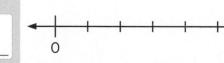

Step In

This game using fractions was designed by Grade 5 students.

For *Fractions Difference*, the fractions are written on the faces of two blank cubes. Both cubes are rolled, and a subtraction equation is written to find the difference between the two fractions.

This table shows each side of the cubes.

Points for denominators

- 1 point if one denominator must be changed to subtract.

- 2 points if both denominators must be changed to subtract.

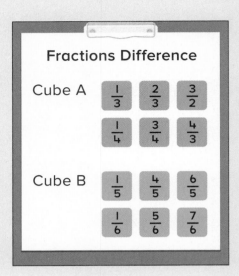

Fractions Difference

Cube A: $\frac{1}{3}$ $\frac{2}{3}$ $\frac{3}{2}$ $\frac{1}{4}$ $\frac{3}{4}$ $\frac{4}{3}$

Cube B: $\frac{1}{5}$ $\frac{4}{5}$ $\frac{6}{5}$ $\frac{1}{6}$ $\frac{5}{6}$ $\frac{7}{6}$

What pairs of fractions could you roll using both the cubes?
What points will you score for the denominators for these rolls? Explain your thinking.

This table shows the scores for each difference.

What pairs of fractions could you roll that will have a difference less than one?

Points for differences

- 1 point if the difference is less than one.

- 2 points if the difference is greater than one.

What pairs of fractions could you roll that will have a difference greater than one?

Step Up

1. Look at both ways of scoring points above. Calculate the total number of points you would make for each of these rolls. Show your thinking.

a. $\frac{3}{2}$ $\frac{7}{6}$

Total score _____

b. $\frac{4}{3}$ $\frac{6}{5}$

Total score _____

c. $\frac{3}{4}$ $\frac{4}{5}$

Total score _____

This game is called *Mixed Numbers Difference*. It is played in the same way as the game described at the top of page 262. Points are scored for denominators and for the total.

Points for denominators	Points for differences
• I point if one denominator must be changed.	• I point if the difference is less than one.
• 2 points if both denominators must be changed.	• 2 points if the difference is greater than one.

2. Read the boxes above to find out how to score points in the game. Then calculate the total number of points that you would make for each of these rolls. Show your thinking.

a. $1\frac{1}{3}$ $2\frac{1}{2}$

Total score _____

b. $3\frac{1}{12}$ $2\frac{2}{3}$

Total score _____

c. $3\frac{2}{3}$ $2\frac{1}{5}$

Total score _____

d. $2\frac{3}{5}$ $3\frac{3}{4}$

Total score _____

Step Ahead   When *Fractions Difference* is played, it is possible to score 2, 3, or 4 points.

Show two different rolls for which you could score 3 points. Then write how you decided which fractions to choose.

Common fractions: Solving word problems involving mixed numbers

Step In

Look at this timesheet.

What is your estimate of the total number of hours that Luis worked? How did you form your estimate?

How would you calculate the exact number of hours?

Donna changed all the fractions to a common denominator. Then she added the fractions and the whole hours.

Describe the steps you think Donna used.

What is an easier way to add the numbers?

Luis's Timesheet	
Monday	$1\frac{1}{4}$ hours
Tuesday	$1\frac{1}{2}$ hours
Wednesday	$1\frac{3}{4}$ hours
Thursday	$\frac{3}{4}$ hour
Friday	$1\frac{1}{2}$ hours

Luis's sister worked $5\frac{3}{4}$ hours on Saturday and $3\frac{3}{4}$ hours on Sunday. How many more hours did she work than Luis?

What steps would you follow to calculate the difference?

Is it possible to calculate the difference without changing either denominator? Explain your thinking.

The difference between 7 hours and $9\frac{1}{2}$ hours is easy to figure out. I can adjust my answer afterward.

Step Up

1. Estimate then solve each problem. Show your thinking.

a. Wendell and Isabelle have some rope that is $9\frac{1}{4}$ yd long. How much more rope do they need to go around a garden that has a perimeter of $13\frac{1}{2}$ yd?

yd

b. Luke buys a piece of wood to make a picture frame that measures $3\frac{3}{4}$ ft by $1\frac{1}{2}$ ft. What was the total length of the piece of wood he buys?

ft

2. Solve these problems. Show your thinking.

a. A punch recipe uses $2\frac{1}{3}$ quarts of pineapple juice. This is $\frac{3}{4}$ of a quart less than the amount of orange juice that is used. How much orange juice is used?

 qt

b. Some edging has been placed on the short side of a triangular-shaped garden. More edging is placed on the other two sides, which are each $8\frac{3}{4}$ yards long. The total edging is $24\frac{2}{12}$ yards long. What is the length of the short side of the garden?

 yd

c. Maka's parcel weighs $4\frac{7}{8}$ lb less than Ruth's parcel, but $2\frac{5}{6}$ more than Anya's parcel. Ruth's parcel weighs $14\frac{3}{8}$ lb. How much does Maka's weigh?

 lb

Step Ahead

Time in hours can be written as common fractions or as decimal fractions. For example, $2\frac{1}{4}$ hours could be written as 2.25 hours.

Rewrite Luis's timesheet as decimal fractions. Then add to find the total hours he worked.

Monday $1\frac{1}{4}$ hours = _____ . _____ hours   Tuesday $1\frac{1}{2}$ hours = _____ . _____ hours

Wednesday $1\frac{3}{4}$ hours = _____ . _____ hours   Thursday $\frac{3}{4}$ hour = _____ . _____ hour

Friday $1\frac{1}{2}$ hours = _____ . _____ hours   Total is _____ hours.

Think and Solve Each ▢ represents the same whole number.

Write the whole numbers that will make both statements true.

$$4 \times \boxed{} + 3 > 31$$

$$5 \times \boxed{} - 4 < 56$$

Words at Work Explain in words two different methods you could use to calculate $4\frac{3}{4} - 2\frac{1}{3}$. Include the answer.

Ongoing Practice

1. Draw jumps on the number line to calculate each difference.

a.

$8.40 - 5.75 =$ [ ]

⟵——————————————————⟶

b.

$6.10 - 3.95 =$ [ ]

⟵——————————————————⟶

2. Estimate, then calculate each difference using mixed numbers. Show your thinking.

a.

$3\frac{2}{3} - 1\frac{1}{5} =$ [ ]

b.

$2\frac{3}{4} - 1\frac{2}{3} =$ [ ]

Preparing for Module 8

Complete each equation.

a.

6   $\frac{1}{8}$

3

3 rows of 6 **and** 3 rows of $\frac{1}{8}$

$(3 \times$ [ ] $) + (3 \times$ ——— $) =$ [ ]

4 rows of 5 **and** 4 rows of $\frac{1}{5}$

$(4 \times$ [ ] $) + (4 \times$ ——— $) =$ [ ]

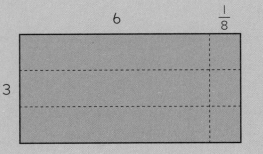

b.

5   $\frac{1}{5}$

4

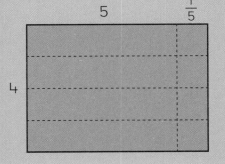

7.9 Number: Building a picture of one billion and beyond

Step In

What is the greatest number you can write on this place-value chart?

Millions			Thousands			Ones		
H	T	O	H	T	O	H	T	O

What are some other multi-digit numbers that you know?

Did you know that one billion $1 bills laid end-to-end would wrap around the equator almost 4 times!

It would take about 32 years to count to one billion if you say one number each second of every day!

How could you extend the place-value chart to show billions?
What place-value abbreviations would you write?

How do you write one billion as a numeral?
What is the relationship between one billion and one million?

Think about one trillion. How would you write the numeral for one trillion?
What is the relationship between one trillion and one million?

Step Up

1. Circle the answer that you think makes sense.

a. The world's population is about ...

8 million   8 billion   8 thousand   8 trillion

b. The number of vehicles on US roads is about ...

300 million   300 billion   300 trillion   300 thousand

c. The distance from Earth to the sun is about ...

150 billion km   150 thousand km   150 trillion km   150 million km

d. One trillion seconds is equivalent to ...

3 years   30 years   30,000 years   3,000 years

2. Write the missing information in the place-value chart.

Billions			Millions								Ones
H		O	H	T	O	H	T	O			O

3. Write **10**, **100**, or **1,000** to complete each statement. Use the place-value chart above to help.

a.

100,000 is _____ **times as much as** 10,000.

b.

1,000,000 is _____ **times as much as** 1,000.

c.

10,000,000 is _____ **times as much as** 1,000,000.

d.

1,000,000,000 is _____ **times as much as** 10,000,000.

e.

10,000,000,000 is _____ **times as much as** 1,000,000,000.

4. Write the numeral to match each number name.

a.	four billion	_____
b.	six million	_____
c.	three trillion	_____

Step Ahead

The height of a stack of 1,000 one-dollar bills is about 4 inches. What is the approximate height of a stack of 1,000,000 one-dollar bills?

_____ feet

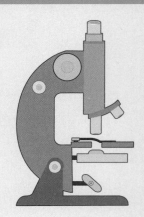

Step In Scientists estimate that there are up to one billion bacteria cells in a single teaspoon of soil.

What numeral would you write to match this number?

We use *billion* to mean 1,000,000,000. In some other countries, billion means 1,000,000,000,000, and they call our billion a *thousand million* or a *milliard*. This can be confusing, so **exponents** are a common way of describing multi-digit numbers.

Exponents are often used to represent multi-digit numbers. They involve repeatedly multiplying a base number. 10^3 is equivalent to $10 \times 10 \times 10$. The 10 is the base and the 3 is the exponent.

Look at the picture below.

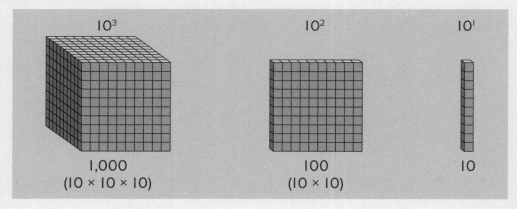

What pattern do you see?
How could you represent 10^4? What would you draw or write?

Think about the number of zeros and the value of the exponent in each number above.
How would you use exponents to write one billion? ... one trillion?

How could you write the number 1 using exponents?

Step Up

1. Write an equation to explain what each of these means.

a.
10^2 _____

b.
10^6 _____

c.
10^5 _____

d.
10^7 _____

2. Draw lines to connect matching values. Not every value has a match.

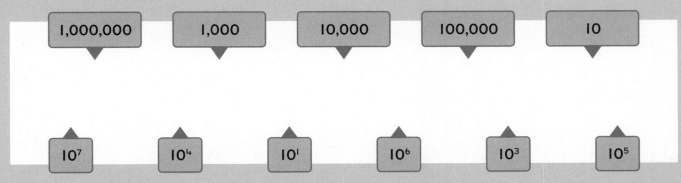

| 1,000,000 | 1,000 | 10,000 | 100,000 | 10 |

| 10^7 | 10^4 | 10^1 | 10^6 | 10^3 | 10^5 |

3. Write each number using exponents.

a. one hundred _____

b. one million _____

c. ten _____

d. ten million _____

e. one _____

f. ten billion _____

Step Ahead

Explain the difference between **expanded notation** and **exponents**.

| **Expanded Notation** |
| $412 = (4 \times 100) + (1 \times 10) + (2 \times 1)$ |

| **Exponents** |
| $1,000 = 10^3$ |

_____
_____
_____
_____
_____

Computation Practice

When Logan went camping he got something. He tried to search for it but brought it home because he couldn't find it. What is it?

★ Complete the equations. Then find each quotient in the grid below and cross out the letter above. Write the remaining letters at the bottom of the page.

$738 \div 6 =$ ___	$296 \div 8 =$ ___	$864 \div 9 =$ ___
$472 \div 8 =$ ___	$378 \div 9 =$ ___	$996 \div 6 =$ ___
$576 \div 9 =$ ___	$888 \div 6 =$ ___	$656 \div 8 =$ ___
$456 \div 8 =$ ___	$992 \div 8 =$ ___	$288 \div 9 =$ ___
$744 \div 8 =$ ___	$198 \div 9 =$ ___	$378 \div 6 =$ ___
$675 \div 9 =$ ___	$564 \div 6 =$ ___	$576 \div 8 =$ ___
$852 \div 6 =$ ___	$368 \div 8 =$ ___	$477 \div 9 =$ ___
$184 \div 8 =$ ___	$774 \div 9 =$ ___	$282 \div 6 =$ ___

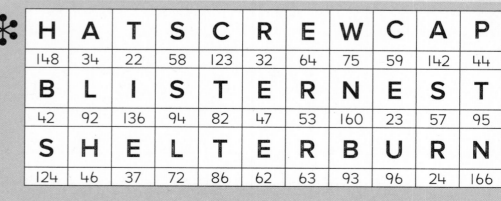

H	A	T	S	C	R	E	W	C	A	P
148	34	22	58	123	32	64	75	59	142	44
B	L	I	S	T	E	R	N	E	S	T
42	92	136	94	82	47	53	160	23	57	95
S	H	E	L	T	E	R	B	U	R	N
124	46	37	72	86	62	63	93	96	24	166

Write the letters in order from the ✻ to the bottom-right corner.

Ongoing Practice

1. a. Find and color an example of each shape in the diagram.

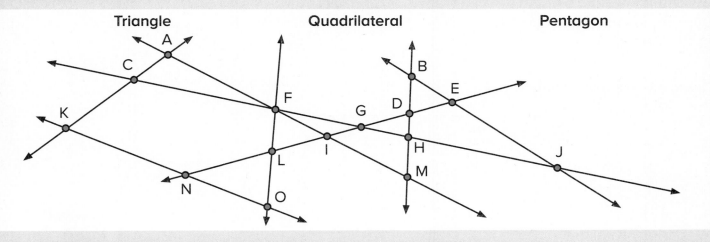

Triangle   Quadrilateral   Pentagon

FROM 4.11.9

b. Write the points that make up the vertices of each shape you find.

Triangle _____   Quadrilateral _____   Pentagon _____

2. Write an equation to explain what each of these means.

FROM 5.7.10

a. 10^2 _____

b. 10^3 _____

c. 10^4 _____

d. 10^5 _____

e. 10^6 _____

Preparing for Module 8

On this number line, the distance from 0 to 1 is one whole. Use the number line to write these mixed numbers as improper fractions.

a. $1\frac{2}{6} = \dfrac{}{}$ **b.** $1\frac{5}{6} = \dfrac{}{}$ **c.** $2\frac{1}{6} = \dfrac{}{}$ **d.** $2\frac{4}{6} = \dfrac{}{}$

Step In

How could you calculate the area of each rectangle?

What equation could you write to show what you did?

A
3 m
21 m

B
3 m
210 m

C
30 m
210 m

Complete this place-value chart.

	Th	H	T	Ones
21 × 3 =				
210 × 3 =				
210 × 30 =				

What do you notice about the products?

How can you use the product for the first equation to figure out the product for the second equation?

Except for the zero, the same digits appear in the products, but in different places.

Step Up

1. Calculate each area. Use a pattern to help you.

a.

32 m
4 m

4 × 32 = _____ m²

320 m
4 m

4 × 320 = _____ m²

320 m
40 m

40 × 320 = _____ m²

b.

5 ft
17 ft

17 × 5 = _____ ft²

5 ft
170 ft

170 × 5 = _____ ft²

50 ft
170 ft

170 × 50 = _____ ft²

2. Use a pattern to help you write the products.

a.

	Th	H	T	Ones
16 × 1 =				
16 × 10 =				
16 × 100 =				

b.

	Th	H	T	Ones
19 × 1 =				
19 × 10 =				
19 × 100 =				

c.

	Th	H	T	Ones
15 × 5 =				
15 × 50 =				
150 × 50 =				

d.

	Th	H	T	Ones
13 × 6 =				
13 × 60 =				
130 × 60 =				

e.

	Th	H	T	Ones
16 × 6 =				
16 × 60 =				
160 × 60 =				

f.

	Th	H	T	Ones
14 × 7 =				
14 × 70 =				
140 × 70 =				

g.

	Th	H	T	Ones
12 × 7 =				
12 × 70 =				
120 × 70 =				

h.

	Th	H	T	Ones
23 × 4 =				
23 × 40 =				
230 × 40 =				

Step Ahead

Write the numbers that are **10 times as much** and **100 times as much**. Then complete each equation.

a.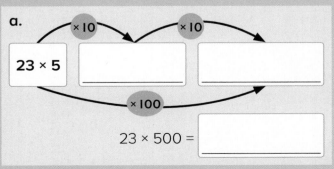

23 × 5

23 × 500 =

b.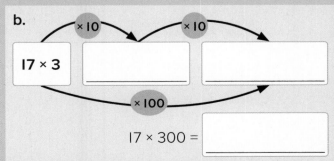

17 × 3

17 × 300 =

Step In

What happens when you multiply a number by 10?

What happens when you multiply a number by 100? What about 1,000?

Think about each product. How do the digits shift?

Multiplying by 10 shifts the digit (7) one place to the left. How many places does the digit shift when you multiply by 100?

Thousands			Ones		
H	T	O	H	T	O
					7
				7	0
			7	0	0

How does this relate to exponents?

Why are these two expressions equivalent?

$$14 \times 1{,}000 = 14 \times 10^3$$

The exponent tells the number of times that the base number (10) is multiplied.
$14 \times 10^3 = 14 \times 10 \times 10 \times 10$

Step Up

1. Complete the missing parts.

a. ⬚ = ⬚ = ⬚

b. $13 \times 1{,}000$ = $13 \times$ ⬚ = ⬚

c. 35×10 = $35 \times$ ⬚ = ⬚

d. $28 \times$ ⬚ = 28×10^4 = ⬚

e. $15 \times$ ⬚ = $15 \times$ ⬚ = 1,500

2. Write each number in expanded form. Then expand the same number with exponents. The first one has been done for you.

a.

5,463

$= (5 \times 1,000) + (4 \times 100) + (6 \times 10) + (3 \times 1)$

$= (5 \times 10^3) + (4 \times 10^2) + (6 \times 10^1) + (3 \times 10^0)$

b.

8,518

$=$ _____

$=$ _____

c.

10,714

$=$ _____

$=$ _____

d.

2,304

$=$ _____

$=$ _____

3. Write the number that has been expanded.

a.

$(7 \times 10^3) + (2 \times 10^2) + (4 \times 10^1) + (9 \times 10^0) =$ _____

b.

$(8 \times 10^3) + (5 \times 10^2) + (7 \times 10^1) + (7 \times 10^0) =$ _____

c.

$(3 \times 10^4) + (9 \times 10^3) + (4 \times 10^1) + (2 \times 10^0) =$ _____

d.

$(5 \times 10^4) + (6 \times 10^2) + (1 \times 10^1) + (8 \times 10^0) =$ _____

Step Ahead

These products added together represent one single number. Calculate the value of each expression, then write the number they represent in total.

7×10^0

5×10^4

8×10^6

1×10^7

3×10^2

_____

Think and Solve

Use the clues to figure out the **greatest** number that could be on the sign? Then write the number.

Clues

- Rounded to the nearest hundred, the number is 200.

- Rounded to the nearest ten, the number is 250.

- Rounded to the nearest one, the number is 250.

Words at Work

Research and write about how exponents are used in everyday life.

Ongoing Practice

I. Look at this diagram.

a. Name two rays that are parallel to each other.

 and _____

b. Name two rays that are perpendicular to each other.

 and _____

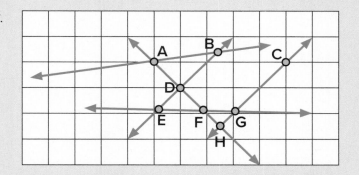

2. Use a pattern to help you write the products.

a.

	Th	H	T	Ones
12 × 2 =				
12 × 20 =				
120 × 20 =				

b.

	Th	H	T	Ones
13 × 4 =				
13 × 40 =				
130 × 40 =				

c.

	Th	H	T	Ones
21 × 4 =				
21 × 40 =				
210 × 40 =				

d.

	Th	H	T	Ones
15 × 3 =				
15 × 30 =				
150 × 30 =				

Preparing for Module 8

Solve each problem. Show your thinking.

a. There are 6 glasses of juice.
Each glass is $\frac{3}{4}$ full.
How much juice is there in total?

_____ glasses of juice

Which whole number
is that closest to? _____

b. Each strip of paper is $\frac{7}{8}$ of a foot long.
Kevin joined 3 strips end-to-end with tape.
What is the total length of the 3 strips?

_____ feet

Which whole number
is that closest to? _____

Step In

Two-thirds of a scoop of laundry detergent is used for each load of laundry. Richard does five loads of laundry.

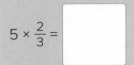

How much laundry detergent does he use?

In the picture below, each large rectangle represents one whole. Richard uses this picture to help solve the problem.

$5 \times \dfrac{2}{3} =$ ☐

How does the picture help solve the problem?
What product should he write?

Giselle uses a different type of laundry detergent. She uses $\dfrac{3}{4}$ of a scoop for each load of laundry. She also does five loads.

In this context, it makes sense to say the product as a mixed number.

How much laundry detergent does she use?

Draw more jumps on this number line to solve the problem. Then complete the equation.

$5 \times \dfrac{3}{4} =$ ☐

Step Up

1. Each large shape is one whole. Shade each shape to match the equation. Then write the product as a common fraction and mixed number.

a.

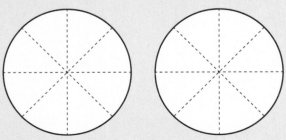

$5 \times \dfrac{3}{8} =$ ☐ $=$ ☐

b.

$7 \times \dfrac{2}{5} =$ ☐ $=$ ☐

2. The distance between each whole number is one whole.
Draw jumps to show the equation. Then write the product.

a.

$3 \times \frac{6}{8} =$ _____

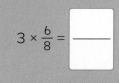

b.

$7 \times \frac{2}{3} =$ _____

c.

$4 \times \frac{3}{5} =$ _____

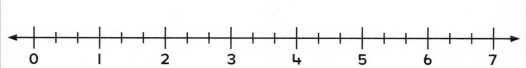

d.

$6 \times \frac{2}{4} =$ _____

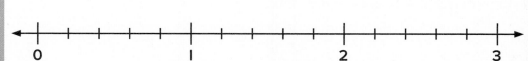

3. Write the product for each of these.

a.

$7 \times \frac{4}{5} =$ _____

b.

_____ $= 14 \times \frac{1}{8}$

c.

$5 \times \frac{5}{6} =$ _____

d.

_____ $= 9 \times \frac{2}{3}$

Step Ahead   Write a word story to match this equation. Then write the product.

$6 \times \frac{3}{5} =$

Step In   One-fourth of these eggs are used to make an omelette.

How many eggs are in the omelette?

The eggs can be shared equally among 4 to find one-fourth.

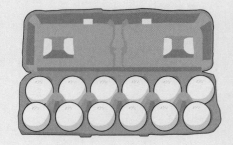

How could you share the eggs to find thirds? What about sixths?

Complete each of these statements.

12 ÷ 4	12 ÷ 3	12 ÷ 2	12 ÷ 6
is equivalent to	is equivalent to	is equivalent to	is equivalent to
⬜/⬜ of 12	⬜/⬜ of 12	⬜/⬜ of 12	⬜/⬜ of 12

How could you use division to calculate $\frac{1}{6}$ of 18?

Multiplication can also be used to calculate the answer. $\frac{1}{6}$ of 18 means $\frac{1}{6} \times 18$, which is $\frac{18}{6}$. The answer is 3.

Step Up   1. Circle the fruit to show the fraction. Then write the division fact you used to figure it out.

a.

$\frac{1}{3}$ of 12 is _____ because

_____

b.

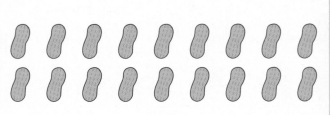

$\frac{1}{3}$ of 18 is _____ because

_____

2. Complete each of these.

a.

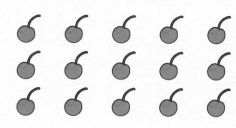

$\frac{1}{5}$ of 15 is _____ because

_____

b.

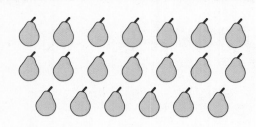

$\frac{1}{5}$ of 20 is _____ because

_____

c.

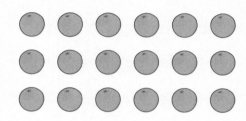

$\frac{1}{6}$ of 18 is _____ because

_____

d.

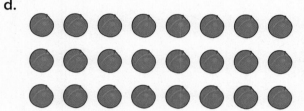

$\frac{1}{6}$ of 24 is _____ because

_____

3. Complete each equation. Then write the division fact you used to solve it.

a.

$\frac{1}{4}$ of 36 = _____

_____

b.

$\frac{1}{8}$ of 48 = _____

_____

c.

$\frac{1}{5}$ of 40 = _____

_____

d.

$\frac{1}{10}$ of 70 = _____

_____

e.

$\frac{1}{3}$ of 27 = _____

_____

f.

$\frac{1}{9}$ of 54 = _____

_____

g.

$\frac{1}{7}$ of 42 = _____

_____

h.

$\frac{1}{12}$ of 60 = _____

_____

Step Ahead   Use what you know about the relationship between unit fractions and division to solve this problem. Show your thinking on page 318.

258 raffle tickets were sold on Thursday. One-third of the tickets were sold before lunch. The rest of the tickets were sold after lunch.

How many tickets were sold before lunch?

_____ tickets

Computation Practice   What can be heard but not seen, and only speaks when spoken to?

★ Complete the equations. Find each total in the grid below and cross out the letter above.
Then write the remaining letters at the bottom of the page.

14.87 + 12.6 = _____

4.5 + 13.72 = _____

14.38 + 6.02 = _____

12.53 + 11.64 = _____

13.56 + 11.7 = _____

5.6 + 14.85 = _____

13.56 + 3.05 = _____

13.47 + 14.72 = _____

12.75 + 12.6 = _____

7.4 + 13.42 = _____

11.74 + 4.5 = _____

10.36 + 18.85 = _____

11.64 + 15.7 = _____

8.3 + 16.38 = _____

13.47 + 5.05 = _____

11.56 + 13.86 = _____

16.84 + 3.5 = _____

5.6 + 14.54 = _____

9.64 + 3.5 = _____

D	A	I	S	Y	C	H	A	I	N
20.45	24.35	20.34	27.47	16.24	25.42	25.35	24.17	24.68	20.58

M	E	D	A	L	C	A	T	C	H
18.22	16.51	29.21	16.61	20.14	19.59	25.26	20.82	18.52	12.69

H	O	O	P	S
27.34	13.14	15.79	20.4	28.19

Write the letters in order from the ✳ to the bottom-right corner.

Ongoing Practice

1. Calculate each total. Show your thinking.

a.
 $3.25 $5.40

$_____

b.
 $4.75 $3.50

$_____

c.
 $6.82 $2.45

$_____

2. Circle fruit to show the fraction. Then write the division fact you used to figure it out.

a.

$\frac{1}{4}$ of 16 is _____ because

_____

b.

$\frac{1}{5}$ of 30 is _____ because

_____

Preparing for Module 9

Write an addition equation to match the jumps on each number line.

a.

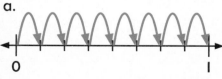

0   1

___ + ___ + ___ + ___ + ___ + ___ + ___ + ___ = ___

b.

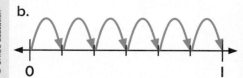

0   1

___ + ___ + ___ + ___ + ___ = ___

Step In   What whole numbers could complete this story?

 There are ___ counters.
$\frac{1}{4}$ of the counters are blue.
The rest of the counters are red.

How many counters are blue?

I think it makes sense to choose a multiple of 4.

Dena chooses 12 as the total number of counters. She solves the problem like this.

$\frac{1}{4}$ of $\boxed{12}$ → $\frac{1}{4} \times \boxed{12}$ = $\boxed{\frac{12}{4}}$

What do you notice about the number of counters chosen and the numerator in the answer box? What do you notice about the denominator?

What do you need to do to record $\frac{12}{4}$ as a whole number?

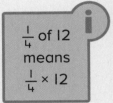

$\frac{1}{4}$ of 12 means $\frac{1}{4} \times 12$

Choose a different total number.
Then write the missing numbers.

$\frac{1}{4}$ of $\boxed{}$ → $\frac{1}{4} \times \boxed{}$ = $\boxed{}$

Without a picture, what helped you calculate how many counters are blue?

What whole number is equivalent to your common fraction?

If I think of a real-life problem, I know that one-fourth of 12 isn't the same as 12 groups of one-fourth. But when I write them as expressions, I know that $\frac{1}{4} \times 12$ has the same product as $12 \times \frac{1}{4}$ because they are turnarounds.

Sometimes it is not easy to think of a fraction of a whole number.
For example, what is $\frac{1}{3}$ of 5?

One method is to think of finding $\frac{1}{3}$ of 1 five times.

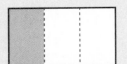 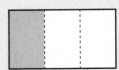 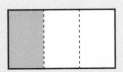 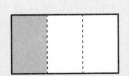 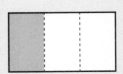

How many thirds are there in total? What is that as a mixed number?

1. Rewrite each sentence as a multiplication equation. Then complete the equation.

a.

$\frac{1}{5}$ of 15 = ☐

_____

b.

$\frac{1}{4}$ of 20 = ☐

_____

c.

$\frac{1}{3}$ of 18 = ☐

_____

d.

$\frac{1}{7}$ of 21 = ☐

_____

e.

$\frac{1}{6}$ of 20 = ☐

_____

f.

$\frac{1}{5}$ of 12 = ☐

_____

2. Solve each problem. Show your thinking.

a. The cost of one hamburger is one-sixth the price of a family meal. What is the cost of one hamburger if the family meal costs $12?

$ _____

b. An 8-oz tub of yogurt costs $2 and a 32-oz tub costs $6. What fraction of the cost of the large tub is the small tub?

3. Solve each problem. Show your thinking.

a.

$\frac{1}{5} \times 40 + 20 =$ _____

b.

$60 \div (12 \times \frac{1}{3}) =$ _____

c.

$4 \times \frac{1}{8} \times 48 =$ _____

Step Ahead

A hiking trail is 15 miles long. The guide says the hikers have only $\frac{1}{4}$ of the distance left to walk. How far do they have left to walk? Write your answer as a mixed number.

 miles

Step In

There are 18 cars in a parking lot. Five-sixths of the cars belong to customers. The rest of the cars belong to staff.

How many cars belong to customers?

Deanna solves the problem like this.

$\frac{1}{6}$ of 18 = 3

because

18 ÷ 6 = 3

so

$\frac{5}{6}$ of 18 = 15

because

5 × 3 = 15

One way to think about this problem is (18 ÷ 6) × 5.

What steps does Deanna take?

How could you use her strategy to calculate $\frac{2}{3}$ of 12?

Step Up

1. Circle the fruit to show the fraction. Then write how you figured it out.

a.

$\frac{3}{5}$ of 10 is _____ because

_____

b.

$\frac{2}{6}$ of 12 is _____ because

_____

c.

$\frac{2}{3}$ of 18 is _____ because

_____

d.

$\frac{3}{4}$ of 20 is _____ because

_____

2. Complete each equation. Show your thinking.

a.

$\frac{3}{5}$ of 15 = _____

b.

$\frac{5}{9}$ of 18 = _____

c.

$\frac{2}{7}$ of 21 = _____

d.

$\frac{3}{4}$ of 16 = _____

3. Solve each problem. Show your thinking.

a. A sheet of stickers is arranged in 2 rows of 6 stickers. Two-thirds of the stickers show animals. How many of the stickers show animals?

_____ stickers

b. Hailey has 30 coins. She makes 5 stacks with the same number of coins in each. 4 stacks have only nickels, and one has 3 other types of coins. How many nickels are there?

_____ nickels

Step Ahead   Complete this number trail.

$\frac{1}{5}$ → ×6 → ____ → + ____ → $\frac{8}{5}$ → ×2 → ____ → − $\frac{1}{10}$ → ____

© ORIGO Education

Think and Solve

This diagram shows the different types of blocks in a set of blocks.

How many blocks are

a. not prisms? _____

b. small blocks? _____

c. not blue? _____

d. either large or blue, or both large and blue? _____

Large		Prisms
20	8	10
8	4	8
	12	
	Blue	30

Words at Work

Write about the different ways you could interpret this equation. Include the answer for each method. Write which method you prefer to use and why.

$\frac{1}{5}$ of 65 = ?

Ongoing Practice

1. Calculate each total. Show your thinking.

a.
40.53 + 12.3 = [_____]

b.
26.5 + 13.12 = [_____]

FROM 5.5.2

2. Circle fruit to show the fraction. Then write an equation to show how you figured it out.

a.

$\frac{3}{5}$ of 20 is _____ because

_____

b.

$\frac{4}{6}$ of 30 is _____ because

_____

FROM 5.8.4

Preparing for Module 9

On this number line, the distance from 0 to 1 is one whole. Use the number line to help you solve each problem.

[number line from 0 to 1]

0   1

a. A stack of blocks is $\frac{1}{2}$ of a foot high. Each block is $\frac{1}{8}$ of a foot high. How many blocks are in the stack?

[____] blocks

b. Some magazines are $\frac{1}{8}$ of an inch thick. How many magazines are needed to make a stack that is $\frac{3}{4}$ of an inch high?

[____] magazines

Step In

Andre races cars. He has 25 miles of the race left to complete. His pit stop crew tell him he has enough fuel to travel $\frac{3}{4}$ of that distance. How many miles can he travel before refueling?

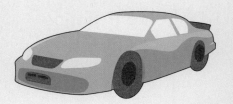

He can drive $\frac{3}{4}$ of 25 miles.
I know how to calculate $\frac{1}{4}$ of 25.
That's $\frac{1}{4} \times 25$.

Katherine showed her thinking like this.

What steps does she follow? Why does she rewrite 25 as $\frac{25}{1}$?
Why does she decide to convert the improper fraction to a mixed number?

$\frac{3}{4}$ of 25

$\frac{3}{4} \times \frac{25}{1} = \frac{75}{4}$

$\frac{75}{4} = 18\frac{3}{4}$

Cole and Sara showed their thinking like this.

Cole	Sara
$\frac{3}{4}$ of 25	$\frac{3}{4}$ of 25
$(3 \times \frac{1}{4}) \times 25 = 3 \times (\frac{1}{4} \times 25)$	$(3 \times \frac{1}{4}) \times 25 = (3 \times 25) \times \frac{1}{4}$
$3 \times (\frac{1}{4} \times 25) = 3 \times \frac{25}{4}$	$(3 \times 25) \times \frac{1}{4} = 75 \times \frac{1}{4}$
$3 \times \frac{25}{4} = \frac{75}{4}$	$75 \times \frac{1}{4} = \frac{75}{4}$
$\frac{75}{4} = 18\frac{3}{4}$	$\frac{75}{4} = 18\frac{3}{4}$

What do all the methods have in common? How are they different?

Why did Cole and Sara change the order of the factors?

Step Up

1. Rewrite each sentence as a multiplication equation. Then complete the equation. Show your thinking.

a.
$\frac{3}{5}$ of 9 =

b.
$\frac{2}{3}$ of 20 =

c.
$\frac{3}{4}$ of 10 =

2. Solve each problem and record your answer as a mixed number. Show your thinking.

a. A bike ride event is 30 miles. A first aid tent is put at the $\frac{3}{4}$ mark of the course. How many miles from the starting point is the first aid tent?

[   ] miles

b. A 20-inch ribbon is cut into eighths, and 3 of the pieces are taped end-to-end. What is the total length of the 3 pieces?

[   ] inches

3. Complete the equation. Then write a word problem to match.

$\frac{3}{4}$ of 15 = [   ]

4. Solve each problem. Show your thinking.

a. $\frac{2}{3} \times 45 \div 5 =$ _____

b. $\frac{8}{10} \times (17 - 12) =$ _____

c. $\frac{3}{5} \times 15 \times 6 =$ _____

Step Ahead

At a pet store, one-fifth of the animals are cats and three-fourths are fish. There are 40 animals at the pet store. How many are not cats or fish? Show your thinking.

[   ]

Step In

Gemma buys a 6-lb bag of food for her four hamsters. Each month they eat $\frac{1}{3}$ of the bag of food. How many pounds of food is eaten after two months? How much food is left in the bag?

Which information is helpful? Which is not helpful? Write an equation to show what each question is asking.

| = ? | | = ? |

Three students thought about the problem in different ways.

Andrea:

Each month for 2 months they ate $\frac{1}{3}$ of 6 lb. I need to find 2 groups of $\frac{1}{3}$ of 6.

That is $2 \times (\frac{1}{3} \times 6) = 4$.

Hunter:

In total they ate $\frac{2}{3}$ of 6 lb. I need to find $\frac{2}{3}$ of 6.

That is $\frac{2}{3} \times 6 = 4$.

Monique:

I would divide 6 lb by 3, then multiply by 2.

That is $(6 \div 3) \times 2 = 4$.

How are the different ways of thinking related to each other?

Which method makes most sense to you?

What picture would you draw to show each method?

Step Up

1. Write an equation to match each problem. Use a letter for the unknown amount.

a. Five-sixths of a pound of turkey is used to make each club sandwich. How much turkey is used to make 6 club sandwiches?

b. Cooper's basketball team scores 60 points. Cooper scores $\frac{1}{4}$ of the points. How many points do the other players on the team score?

c. It takes $\frac{1}{4}$ of an hour to bake a tray of cookies. How long will it take to bake 5 trays of cookies, one after the other?

d. A large bottle of juice costs $8 and a small bottle costs $2. What fraction of the cost of the large bottle is the cost of the small one?

2. Solve each problem. Show your thinking.

a. Jessica's cat weighs 7 lb. The neighbor's cat weighs $\frac{1}{5}$ more than Jessica's cat. How much does the neighbor's cat weigh?

 lb

b. It is 20 miles from the airport to the hotel. The driver says that there is $\frac{1}{8}$ of the total distance left to travel. What distance has already been driven?

mi

c. Sliced cheese comes in $\frac{3}{4}$ lb packs. James has 2 boxes with 30 packs of cheese in each box. What is the total mass of the cheese in the boxes?

 lb

d. Ricardo made a data table with 4 rows and 10 columns. He colors $\frac{3}{8}$ of the cells yellow. What number of cells are yellow?

 cells

3. Write **true** or **false** beside each statement.

a. $\frac{1}{3} \times (5 + 2)$ is one-third of $5 + 2$.

b. $6 \times \frac{3}{4}$ is six times as much as $\frac{1}{4}$.

c. $\frac{1}{9} \times 7 \times 3$ is nine times as much as 7×3.

Step Ahead

Caleb pours 54 liters of water into an empty barrel and notes it is now $\frac{6}{8}$ full. How many liters will the barrel hold when it is full? Show your thinking.

_____ L

Computation Practice   Why should a golfer wear two pairs of shorts?

⭐ Complete the equations. Then write each letter above its matching product at the bottom of the page.

27 × 33 = _____ **i**

34 × 15 = _____ **n**

24 × 32 = _____ **e**

28 × 12 = _____ **t**

25 × 48 = _____ **h**

33 × 14 = _____ **l**

35 × 25 = _____ **i**

15 × 41 = _____ **m**

48 × 12 = _____ **g**

22 × 44 = _____ **g**

42 × 21 = _____ **t**

45 × 13 = _____ **a**

16 × 23 = _____ **e**

18 × 41 = _____ **e**

22 × 37 = _____ **e**

31 × 26 = _____ **h**

19 × 21 = _____ **n**

13 × 26 = _____ **o**

21 × 28 = _____ **h**

17 × 26 = _____ **o**

1,200	768	615	891	968	806	336	576	814	882

585		588	338	462	368	875	510	442	399	738

Ongoing Practice

1. Calculate the total mass of these packages.

a.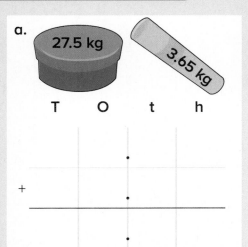

27.5 kg 3.65 kg

T O t h

+

b.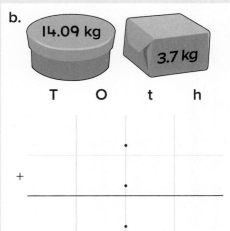

14.09 kg 3.7 kg

T O t h

+

c.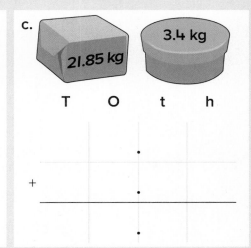

21.85 kg 3.4 kg

T O t h

+

FROM 5.5.3

2. Write an equation to match each problem. Use a letter for the unknown amount.

a. A fun run is 5 kilometers long. Gavin has run $\frac{2}{3}$ of the distance. How far does he have left to run?

b. Mary's team scores 18 points in the first half and 7 points in the second half. Mary scored a total of 5 points. What fraction of the total points did Mary score?

c. It takes $\frac{3}{4}$ of an hour to bake a cake. How long will it take to bake 6 cakes one after the other?

d. Daniela buys 6 lb of sausages. Only $\frac{5}{8}$ of the sausages are used. How many pounds of sausages were used?

FROM 5.8.6

Preparing for Module 9

Think multiplication to calculate the missing dimension. Write the equations to match.

a.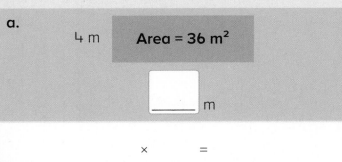

4 m Area = 36 m²

_____ m

_____ × _____ = _____

_____ ÷ _____ = _____

b.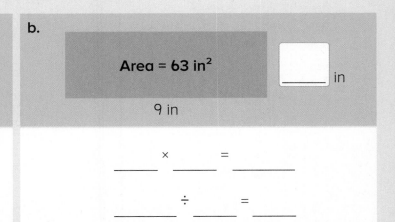

Area = 63 in²

_____ in

9 in

_____ × _____ = _____

_____ ÷ _____ = _____

Step In

A new housing development is being built on a large rectangular block of land. The land is $\frac{2}{3}$ of a mile by $\frac{3}{4}$ of a mile.

How could you use this diagram to calculate the area of the development?

$$\frac{2}{3} \times \frac{3}{4} = ?$$

To find the area of a rectangle, I need to multiply the dimensions.

Each of these fractions is a dimension of the total area.

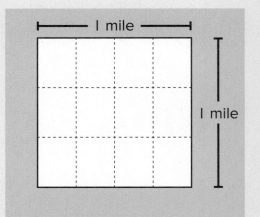

William labeled the dimensions and shaded the rectangle. How does the diagram on the right match the equation above?

How many equal parts divide the whole square?
How many of these parts did William shade?
What is the area of the housing development?

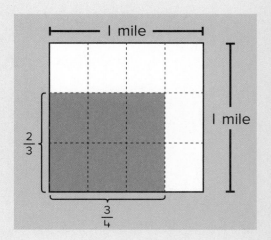

Step Up

1. Calculate the products. Label the dimensions and shade the array to show your thinking.

a.

$$\frac{1}{3} \times \frac{1}{4} = \underline{}$$

b.

$$\frac{2}{3} \times \frac{2}{3} = \underline{}$$

c.

$$\frac{1}{4} \times \frac{1}{4} = \underline{}$$

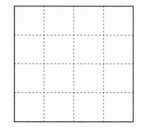

2. Draw and color an array to match each equation. Then write the product.

a.

$$\frac{3}{8} \times \frac{3}{4} = \underline{\quad}$$

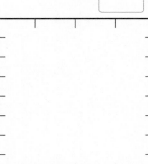

b.

$$\frac{5}{8} \times \frac{2}{3} = \underline{\quad}$$

c.

$$\frac{5}{6} \times \frac{3}{4} = \underline{\quad}$$

d.

$$\frac{4}{5} \times \frac{3}{6} = \underline{\quad}$$

e.

$$\frac{3}{5} \times \frac{2}{3} = \underline{\quad}$$

f.

$$\frac{2}{5} \times \frac{1}{4} = \underline{\quad}$$

Step Ahead

Kinu is looking at two coffee table tops. The **teak** table is $\frac{4}{5}$ yard long and $\frac{2}{3}$ yard wide. The **oak** table top is $\frac{7}{9}$ yard long and $\frac{2}{5}$ yard wide.

Which coffee table has the greater area? _____ By how much? _____ yd²
Show your thinking.

Common fractions: Multiplying two common fractions symbolically

Step In

David was thinking about multiplying $\frac{1}{2} \times \frac{1}{5}$ and noticed something interesting.

$$\frac{1}{2} \times \frac{1}{5} = \frac{1}{10}$$

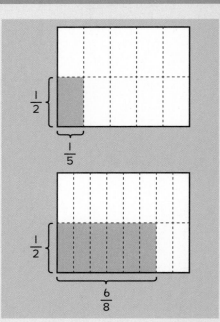

What do you think he noticed about the numerators and denominators?

He decided to check his thinking with another problem.

$$\frac{1}{2} \times \frac{6}{8} = \frac{6}{16}$$

To find the product of two fractions, multiply the numerators then multiply the denominators. The two products form a fraction that shows the overall product.

Trina is playing a game.

She rolls each cube, then multiplies the two numbers she rolls.
How could you use David's observation to calculate the product?

Trina rolls the two cubes again.
How would you calculate the product of her second roll?

Sometimes it's easier to work with unit fractions. $5 \times (7 \times \frac{1}{5})$ is equivalent to $(5 \times \frac{1}{5}) \times 7$. That's 1×7 so the product is 7.

Step Up

1. Calculate the product of each roll. Show your thinking.

a. $\frac{4}{1}$ $\frac{1}{8}$

b. $\frac{4}{6}$ $\frac{2}{3}$

c. $\frac{5}{2}$ $\frac{7}{5}$

2. Your teacher will give you two cubes. Roll the cubes and write the numbers you roll. Then calculate the products.

a.

b.

c.

d.

e.

f.

3. Complete each equation.

a. $\dfrac{2}{5} \times \dfrac{7}{3} = \boxed{}$

b. $\boxed{} \times \dfrac{4}{1} = \dfrac{8}{5}$

c. $\dfrac{10}{3} = \boxed{} \times \dfrac{2}{3}$

d. $\boxed{} \times \dfrac{6}{5} = \dfrac{18}{5}$

e. $\dfrac{4}{6} = \boxed{} \times \dfrac{1}{2}$

f. $5 = \dfrac{1}{4} \times \boxed{}$

Step Ahead

A narrow garden bed has an area of 15 square yards. The short sides of the bed are each $\dfrac{3}{4}$ yard wide.

What is the length of each long side?

Show your thinking.

Hint: Convert 15 to a common fraction that has a denominator of 4.

$\underline{\hspace{2cm}}$ yd

Think and Solve Same shapes are the same number of kilograms.

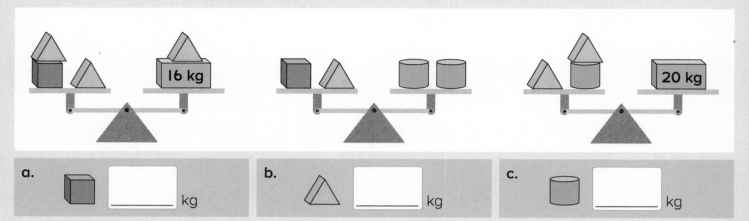

a. _____ kg

b. _____ kg

c. _____ kg

Words at Work Write a word problem that involves fractions and two different operations. Then describe how you would solve the problem.

Ongoing Practice

1. Estimate the perimeter in your head. Then use the standard algorithm to calculate the exact perimeter.

a.

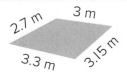

b.

c.

2. Draw and color an array to match each equation. Then write the product.

a.

$$\frac{2}{6} \times \frac{3}{4} = \frac{\quad}{\quad}$$

b.

$$\frac{6}{8} \times \frac{1}{3} = \frac{\quad}{\quad}$$

c.

$$\frac{4}{5} \times \frac{1}{4} = \frac{\quad}{\quad}$$

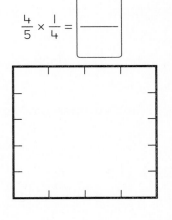

Preparing for Module 9

Complete each of these.

a.   1 meter

is equivalent to

_____ centimeters

is equivalent to

_____ millimeters

b.   5 meters

is equivalent to

_____ centimeters

is equivalent to

_____ millimeters

c.   10 meters

is equivalent to

_____ centimeters

is equivalent to

_____ millimeters

Step In

Potato salad is sold in 3 lb tubs. Allison uses $1\frac{1}{4}$ tubs.
How many pounds of potato salad did she use in total?

> I tub is 3 lb so I know at least 3 lb are used.

Sofia converts each number to an improper fraction.

$1\frac{1}{4}$ of 3

$\frac{5}{4}$ of 3

$\frac{5}{4} \times \frac{3}{1} = \frac{15}{4}$

$\frac{15}{4} = 3\frac{3}{4}$

Felipe breaks the numbers into parts to multiply.

$1\frac{1}{4} \times 3 = (1 + \frac{1}{4}) \times 3$

$(1 + \frac{1}{4}) \times 3 = (1 \times 3) + (\frac{1}{4} \times 3)$

$(1 \times 3) + (\frac{1}{4} \times 3) = 3 + \frac{3}{4}$

$3 + \frac{3}{4} = 3\frac{3}{4}$

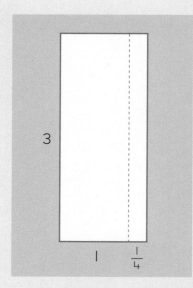

The diagram on the right shows Felipe's thinking.
What totals should go inside each section?

What steps does each person follow?

Which method do you prefer? Why?

How could you use each method to calculate $2\frac{1}{5} \times 4$?

Step Up

1. Write the missing numbers. Then complete the equation.

a.

$3 \times 4\frac{1}{4} = \boxed{}$

3

4   $\frac{1}{4}$

$(3 \times \boxed{}) + (3 \times \boxed{})$

b.

$4\frac{3}{5} \times 2 = \boxed{}$

2

4   $\frac{3}{5}$

$(2 \times \boxed{}) + (2 \times \boxed{})$

2. For each of these, calculate the product in two ways.

a.

$5 \times 2\frac{1}{3}$

Multiply the parts	Use improper fractions

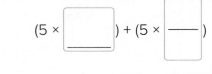

$(5 \times \underline{}) + (5 \times \dfrac{}{})$

$\dfrac{}{} + \dfrac{}{} = \boxed{}$

$\dfrac{5}{1} \times \dfrac{}{} = \dfrac{}{}$

b.

$3 \times 4\frac{3}{4}$

Multiply the parts	Use improper fractions

c.

$4 \times 2\frac{2}{5}$

Multiply the parts	Use improper fractions

Step Ahead

Multiply the two numbers across each row to find the product in the matching circle. Multiply the two numbers down each column to find the product in the matching circle.

a.

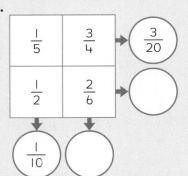

b.

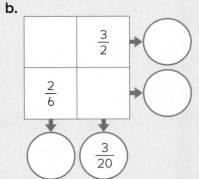

c.

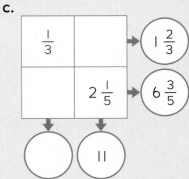

Step In

Jamal buys $1\frac{2}{3}$ pounds of cooked turkey meat. $\frac{3}{4}$ of the meat is used to make sandwiches.

TURKEY MEAT

$1\frac{2}{3}$ lb

How many pounds of turkey are used to make sandwiches?

I have to calculate $\frac{3}{4}$ of $1\frac{2}{3}$. It sounds hard, but converting the mixed number to an improper fraction makes it easier.

Pati calculates the answer like this.

What steps does she follow?

How does converting the mixed number to an improper fraction help to calculate the product?

What is another way to say the product?

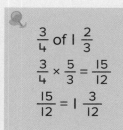

$\frac{3}{4}$ of $1\frac{2}{3}$

$\frac{3}{4} \times \frac{5}{3} = \frac{15}{12}$

$\frac{15}{12} = 1\frac{3}{12}$

$\frac{3}{12}$ is equivalent to $\frac{1}{4}$, so $1\frac{3}{12}$ is equal to $1\frac{1}{4}$.

How could you use the same strategy to calculate $\frac{5}{3}$ of $2\frac{1}{2}$?

Step Up

1. Rewrite each equation by converting each mixed number to an improper fraction. Then write the product.

a.
$\frac{3}{5} \times 1\frac{1}{2} =$

b.
$2\frac{1}{2} \times \frac{5}{6} =$

c.
$\frac{5}{4} \times 1\frac{1}{3} =$

d.
$\frac{4}{6} \times 1\frac{3}{4} =$

e.
$3\frac{1}{4} \times \frac{1}{2} =$

f.
$3\frac{1}{3} \times \frac{6}{5} =$

2. Solve each problem. Show your thinking.

a. Paul buys $3\frac{1}{2}$ lb of potatoes. $\frac{2}{5}$ of the potatoes are used to make a potato bake. How many pounds of potatoes are used?

☐ lb

b. Jude can walk about $4\frac{1}{2}$ miles in one hour. On Monday, he walks for $\frac{3}{4}$ of an hour. How many miles does he walk?

☐ mi

c. A small, rectangular wildlife park has opened in the city. It is $\frac{2}{3}$ of a mile wide, and $2\frac{1}{2}$ miles long. What is the area of the park?

☐ mi²

d. Each bottle of detergent holds $\frac{1}{2}$ quart. The school cafeteria uses $2\frac{1}{3}$ bottles each week. How many quarts of detergent are used each week?

☐ qt

Step Ahead   Complete each equation. Then write what you notice.

a. $\frac{2}{5} \times \frac{5}{2} = $ ☐

b. $\frac{9}{6} \times \frac{6}{9} = $ ☐

c. $\frac{1}{8} \times \frac{8}{1} = $ ☐

Computation Practice

★ Complete the equations. Then write each letter above its matching difference at the bottom of the page to discover a fact about the natural world.

35 − 7.8 = _____ **l**	25 − 6.7 = _____ **t**	27 − 8.8 = _____ **s**
23 − 6.5 = _____ **m**	28 − 4.8 = _____ **l**	21 − 5.8 = _____ **v**
42 − 6.9 = _____ **e**	34 − 8.8 = _____ **h**	41 − 6.7 = _____ **a**
33 − 4.6 = _____ **y**	43 − 8.5 = _____ **d**	22 − 6.9 = _____ **e**
18 − 4.7 = _____ **e**	26 − 7.9 = _____ **e**	40 − 5.9 = _____ **h**
35 − 6.7 = _____ **e**	36 − 8.9 = _____ **e**	34 − 2.8 = _____ **i**
42 − 7.8 = _____ **r**	23 − 5.6 = _____ **a**	27 − 9.8 = _____ **c**
51 − 7.5 = _____ **s**		

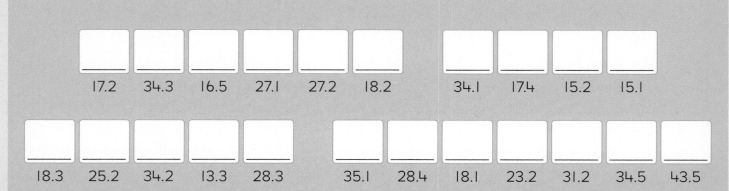

17.2	34.3	16.5	27.1	27.2	18.2	34.1	17.4	15.2	15.1

18.3	25.2	34.2	13.3	28.3	35.1	28.4	18.1	23.2	31.2	34.5	43.5

1. Draw the reflection on the other side of the dashed line.

a.

b.

c.

2. Calculate each product. Show your thinking.

a.
$$3 \times 2\frac{3}{4} = \boxed{}$$

b.
$$2 \times 4\frac{3}{5} = \boxed{}$$

c.
$$6 \times 1\frac{1}{4} = \boxed{}$$

d.
$$3 \times 1\frac{4}{6} = \boxed{}$$

Preparing for Module 9   Write the equivalent mass in grams.

a.   3 kilograms

is the same mass as

_____ g

b. $2\frac{1}{4}$ kilograms

is the same mass as

_____ g

c. $1\frac{8}{10}$ kilograms

is the same mass as

_____ g

Step In

Franco and Alisa have created a multiplication game that uses two number cubes.

They have written whole numbers on one cube and fractions on the other cube. They roll both cubes and multiply the whole number by the fraction.

Here is the way they scored points:

- A product greater than the whole number scores 1 point.
- A product equal to the whole number scores 2 points.
- A product less than the whole number scores 3 points.

What are some different multiplication equations Franco and Alisa could write for the numbers you can see on the cubes?

What will be the score for each of these equations?

$5 \times \frac{3}{4} =$ _____ $4 \times \frac{3}{2} =$ _____

Why does the expression $6 \times \frac{4}{4}$ score 2 points?

Step Up

1. Complete each equation.

a. $\frac{3}{4} \times \frac{2}{5} =$ _____

b. $\frac{4}{3} \times \frac{1}{6} =$ _____

c. $\frac{6}{6} \times \frac{3}{8} =$ _____

d. $12 \times \frac{1}{3} =$ _____

2. Look at each equation from Question 1. Write equivalent fractions so it is easy to compare the product with the first factor.

a. first factor: _____   product: _____

b. first factor: _____   product: _____

c. first factor: _____   product: _____

d. first factor: _____   product: _____

3. Look at your answers for Questions 1 and 2. Write **less than**, **equal to**, or **greater than** to complete the statement below so that it is true for all the equations in Question 1.

If the first factor is multiplied by a number less than one

_____

the product will be _____ the first factor.

© ORIGO Education

4. Complete each equation.

a.

$$\frac{5}{6} \times \frac{4}{3} = \boxed{}$$

b.

$$\frac{1}{2} \times \frac{6}{4} = \boxed{}$$

c.

$$\frac{7}{10} \times \frac{4}{2} = \boxed{}$$

d.

$$6 \times \frac{8}{3} = \boxed{}$$

5. Look at each equation from Question 4. Write equivalent fractions so that it is easy to compare the product with the first factor.

a.
first factor: ——— $\boxed{}$

product: ——— $\boxed{}$

b.
first factor: ——— $\boxed{}$

product: ——— $\boxed{}$

c.
first factor: ——— $\boxed{}$

product: ——— $\boxed{}$

d.
first factor: ——— $\boxed{}$

product: ——— $\boxed{}$

6. Look at your answers for Questions 4 and 5. Write **less than**, **equal to**, or **greater than** to complete the statement below so that it is true for all the equations in Question 4.

If the first factor is multiplied by a number greater than one

$$\boxed{}$$

the product will be $\underline{}$ the first factor.

7. Identify whether the product will be **less than**, **equal to**, or **greater than** the first factor. You do not need to actually calculate the product.

a. $\frac{14}{19} \times \frac{32}{28}$

- ◯ less than
- ◯ equal to
- ◯ greater than

b. $\frac{23}{23} \times \frac{36}{41}$

- ◯ less than
- ◯ equal to
- ◯ greater than

c. $\frac{26}{17} \times \frac{53}{65}$

- ◯ less than
- ◯ equal to
- ◯ greater than

d. $\frac{47}{23} \times \frac{47}{23}$

- ◯ less than
- ◯ equal to
- ◯ greater than

e. $3 \times \frac{76}{89}$

- ◯ less than
- ◯ equal to
- ◯ greater than

f. $\frac{1}{52} \times 8$

- ◯ less than
- ◯ equal to
- ◯ greater than

g. $\frac{3}{9} \times \frac{9}{3}$

- ◯ less than
- ◯ equal to
- ◯ greater than

h. $7\frac{18}{26} \times \frac{2}{65}$

- ◯ less than
- ◯ equal to
- ◯ greater than

Step Ahead

Complete each equation so the product is greater than the first factor.

a.

$$\frac{3}{5} \times \frac{\boxed{}}{\underline{}} = \underline{}\,\boxed{}$$

b.

$$\frac{8}{10} \times \frac{\boxed{}}{\underline{}} = \underline{}\,\boxed{}$$

c.

$$\frac{\boxed{}}{\underline{}} \times \frac{9}{4} = \underline{}\,\boxed{}$$

d.

$$2\frac{5}{6} \times \frac{\boxed{}}{\underline{}} = \underline{}\,\boxed{}$$

Step In

This recipe makes one large bowl of punch.

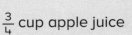

Fruit Punch

$\frac{3}{4}$ cup apple juice

$\frac{3}{4}$ cup water

$2\frac{1}{4}$ cups orange juice

$1\frac{1}{2}$ cups pineapple juice

2 cups iced tea

Callum wants to make three bowls.

How would you calculate the total amount of each ingredient he will need to make the punch?

He is making 3 bowls of punch, so that is like multiplying by 3.

Jayden decides to use $1\frac{1}{2}$ times the recipe to make extra punch.
He wrote this equation to calculate the amount of apple juice.

Why did he change $1\frac{1}{2}$ to $\frac{3}{2}$ to multiply?

$$\frac{3}{4} \times \frac{3}{2} = \boxed{}$$

What equations would you write to calculate the other ingredient amounts he will need?

How much will he need of each ingredient to make $1\frac{1}{2}$ times the recipe?

Step Up

1. Calculate each length. Show your thinking. You can draw a picture to help.

a. Victoria has 5 blue ribbons that are each $1\frac{3}{4}$ yd long. If another ribbon is 6 times as long as one of Victoria's ribbons, what is its length?

$\boxed{}$ yd

b. Evan is making a square picture frame. The length of a side is $2\frac{2}{3}$ ft. What is the total length of timber he needs?

$\boxed{}$ ft

2. Solve each problem. Show your thinking.

a. Bianca reads $\frac{3}{4}$ of a page of a book each minute. She has 25 pages left to read. How many pages will she read in $5\frac{1}{2}$ minutes?

 pages

b. A large housing development is $\frac{4}{5}$ of a mile wide by $\frac{3}{4}$ of a mile long. There are 14 houses in the development. What is the area of the development?

 mi²

c. A dance floor is rectangular in shape. Its length is $15\frac{1}{2}$ feet. Its width is $\frac{2}{3}$ of the length. What is the width of the floor in feet?

ft

d. Nam works $1\frac{3}{4}$ hours each day at his part-time job. He is paid $8 for each hour. Bella earns 3 times as much as Nam each day. How much does she earn in one day?

$_____

Step Ahead

A small table top measures $2\frac{3}{4}$ ft by $3\frac{2}{3}$ ft. The dimensions of a large table top are double those of the small table. How many times greater is the area of the large table top than the small table top? Use page 319 if needed.

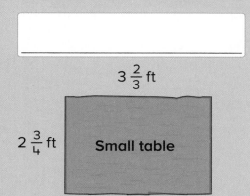

$3\frac{2}{3}$ ft

$2\frac{3}{4}$ ft Small table

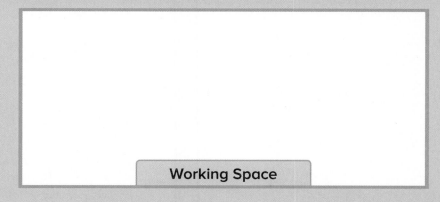

Working Space

© ORIGO Education

Think and Solve

THINK TANK

Here, means **halve the second factor then subtract the first factor.**

$$3 @ 16 = 5$$

Look at these and figure out what ✳ is doing.

2 ✳ 3 = 14	1 ✳ 10 = 41	5 ✳ 1 = 9	6 ✳ 6 = 30

Complete these.

a. 7 ✳ 0 = _____

b. 6 ✳ 2 = _____

c. _____ ✳ 4 = 19

d. What is ✳ doing ? _____

_____

Words at Work

Write in words how you solve this problem.

Costumes are being made for a school production. Each knight costume needs $1\frac{1}{3}$ yards of silver fabric and $2\frac{1}{2}$ feet of silver braid. There are 11 knights in the production. Each royal costume takes $2\frac{2}{3}$ yards of satin and $4\frac{3}{4}$ feet of gold braid. There are 12 costumes, 6 in yellow satin, and 6 in blue satin. Satin is sold at \$5 a yard, braid costs \$2 a foot, and the silver fabric costs \$3.50 a yard. How much of each type of fabric and braid needs to be bought? What is the total cost?

© ORIGO Education

Ongoing Practice

1. Draw the line of symmetry in each shape.

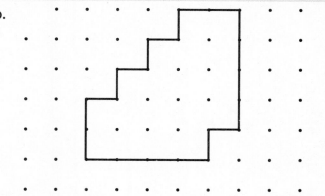

a.

b.

2. Identify whether the product will be **less than**, **equal to**, or **greater than** the first factor.
   You do not need to actually calculate the product.

a.	b.	c.	d.
$\frac{4}{9} \times \frac{12}{20}$	$\frac{23}{4} \times \frac{41}{41}$	$\frac{8}{15} \times \frac{23}{5}$	$\frac{27}{33} \times \frac{67}{12}$
○ less than	○ less than	○ less than	○ less than
○ equal to	○ equal to	○ equal to	○ equal to
○ greater than	○ greater than	○ greater than	○ greater than

e.	f.	g.	h.
$\frac{3}{6} \times 6$	$\frac{12}{52} \times \frac{8}{10}$	$\frac{4}{9} \times \frac{3}{3}$	$7\frac{15}{29} \times \frac{27}{55}$
○ less than	○ less than	○ less than	○ less than
○ equal to	○ equal to	○ equal to	○ equal to
○ greater than	○ greater than	○ greater than	○ greater than

Preparing for Module 9   Write the equivalent capacity in milliliters.

a.	b.	c.
4 liters	9 liters	$2\frac{1}{4}$ liters
is equivalent to	is equivalent to	is equivalent to
_____ mL	_____ mL	_____ mL

d.	e.	f.
$2\frac{7}{10}$ liters	$6\frac{1}{10}$ liters	$4\frac{9}{10}$ liters
is equivalent to	is equivalent to	is equivalent to
_____ mL	_____ mL	_____ mL

Step In

These two pizzas must be shared equally among five friends.

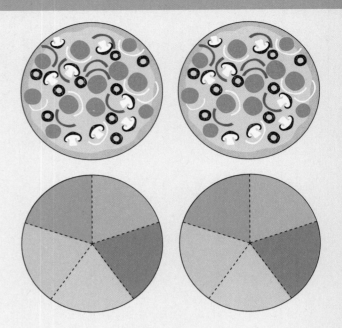

How much pizza should each person get?

Valentina drew a picture to show her thinking.

How many pizzas need to be shared? ▢

How many people shared the pizzas? ▢

So how much pizza in total will each person get? ▢

Sharing among five is the same as finding one-fifth.
If $1 \div 5 = \frac{1}{5}$, then $2 \div 5 = \frac{1}{5} + \frac{1}{5}$.
That is equivalent to $\frac{2}{5}$.

The **numerator** tells the number of objects to be shared. The **denominator** tells the number of shares.

Noah drew a slightly different picture to represent the problem.

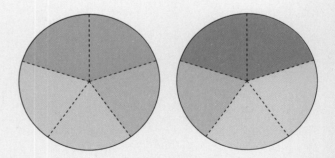

What is the same about his and Valentina's pictures?

How are they different?

Step Up

1. Color the diagram to solve this problem. Then write the missing numbers.

2 slices of banana bread are shared equally by 3 people.
How much of one whole slice will be in each share?

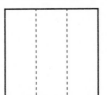

▢ slices shared by

▢ people

$2 \div \dfrac{}{} = \dfrac{}{}$

2. Each large rectangle below is one whole. Complete the sentence and color the diagram to show each share.

a. $\frac{3}{5}$ is equivalent to

[___] divided by [___]

b. $\frac{4}{7}$ is equivalent to

[___] divided by [___]

3. Solve each problem. Draw a picture to show your thinking.

a. 3 platters of fruit are shared equally among 8 people. What fraction of a whole platter is in each share?

[___] platter

b. 4 families equally share 5 liters of juice. How much juice does each family receive?

[___] liters

Step Ahead   Each common fraction below is the result of division. Write word problems to match.

a.

$\frac{3}{4}$

_____

_____

b.

$1\frac{1}{2}$

_____

_____

Step In

Ryan has 2 one-quart pitchers of milk to pour into some cups.

Each cup holds $\frac{1}{4}$ of a quart. How many cups can be filled?

What division equation represents this problem?

☐ ÷ ☐/☐ = **?**

Use the diagram above to calculate the number of cups that can be filled.

Write the completed equation.

☐ ÷ ☐/☐ = ☐

How could you use multiplication to check whether the quotient is correct?

> If I multiply the amount in each cup by the number of cups, I should get the number of pitchers as the result. That will tell me if the quotient is correct.

Step Up

1. Each large rectangle below represents one whole. Shade the number of whole shapes. Then draw lines to split each shape into parts to match the fraction. Complete each equation.

a. Shade 5 whole shapes.
How many thirds are in 5?

$5 \div \frac{1}{3} =$ ☐

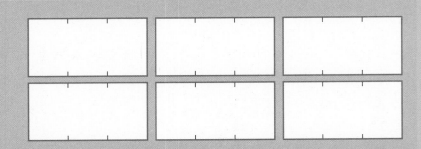

b. Shade 6 whole shapes.
How many fourths are in 6?

$6 \div \frac{1}{4} =$ ☐

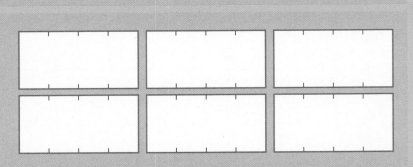

2. Solve each problem. Use the pictures to help you, then complete the equation.

a. 5 loaves of banana bread are cut into fourths. How many pieces are there?

 ÷ _____ = _____

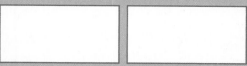

b. Four 1-ft ribbons are each cut into thirds. How many pieces of ribbon are there?

 ÷ _____ = _____

3. Use multiplication to check these answers to division problems.

a.
$$4 \div \frac{1}{5} = 20$$

○ Correct   ○ Incorrect

b.
$$12 \div \frac{1}{4} = 3$$

○ Correct   ○ Incorrect

c.
$$10 \div \frac{1}{6} = 60$$

○ Correct   ○ Incorrect

d.
$$8 \div \frac{1}{4} = 2$$

○ Correct   ○ Incorrect

Step Ahead

Arianna baked some cherry pies. She cut them into 12 equal-sized pieces. What could have been the number of whole pies and the fraction she used to divide the pieces? Write equations to show different possible solutions.

Computation Practice

Who was the first President to live in the White House?

⭐ Complete the equations. Then find each answer in the puzzle below and shade the matching letter. The remaining letters spell the answer.

$1\frac{5}{8} + \frac{5}{8} =$ ☐	$1\frac{3}{8} - \frac{5}{8} =$ ☐	$1\frac{3}{5} + 1\frac{3}{5} =$ ☐	$2\frac{3}{6} - 1\frac{5}{6} =$ ☐
$1\frac{1}{6} - \frac{4}{6} =$ ☐	$\frac{7}{12} + \frac{11}{12} =$ ☐	$3 - \frac{4}{5} =$ ☐	$2\frac{3}{8} + 1\frac{2}{8} =$ ☐
$\frac{7}{10} + 1\frac{1}{10} =$ ☐	$1\frac{1}{10} - \frac{7}{10} =$ ☐	$1\frac{1}{6} - \frac{5}{6} =$ ☐	$\frac{4}{5} + 1\frac{4}{5} =$ ☐
$\frac{3}{8} + 2\frac{7}{8} =$ ☐	$1\frac{7}{12} - \frac{11}{12} =$ ☐	$\frac{4}{5} + 1\frac{3}{5} =$ ☐	$1\frac{3}{8} - \frac{4}{8} =$ ☐
$\frac{1}{6} + 1\frac{5}{6} =$ ☐	$2\frac{1}{8} - 1\frac{4}{8} =$ ☐	$1\frac{9}{12} + 1\frac{9}{12} =$ ☐	$3\frac{4}{5} - 3\frac{2}{5} =$ ☐

ORIGO Stepping Stones · Grade 5 · 9.2

© ORIGO Education

Ongoing Practice

1. Calculate the difference between each pair of prices. Show your thinking.

a.

$3.51 $9.75

$ _____

b.

$7.24 $4.03

$ _____

2. Each large rectangle below represents one whole. Shade the number of whole shapes. Then draw lines to split each shape into parts to match the fraction. Complete each equation.

a. Shade 4 whole shapes.
   How many thirds are in 4?

   $4 \div \frac{1}{3} =$ _____

b. Shade 5 whole shapes.
   How many fourths are in 5?

   $5 \div \frac{1}{4} =$ _____

Preparing for Module 10

The distance between 0 and 1 is one whole. Write the decimal fraction shown by each arrow.

a. _____   b. _____   c. _____   d. _____

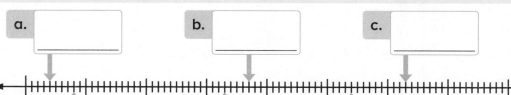

0   1

e. _____   f. _____   g. _____   h. _____

Step In

Janice has baked four large trays of cornbread.
She cuts each tray into thirds to sell in separate packets at a bake sale.
How many packets does she have?

Mmmm. How many one-thirds are in 4?

I know there are 3 one-thirds in 1, so if each tray has 3, there must be 12 one-thirds in 4 trays of cornbread.

Write numbers to show this thinking.

see $\quad 4 \div \dfrac{1}{3} = \boxed{}$

think $\quad 4 \times (1 \div \dfrac{1}{3}) = \boxed{}$

Step Up

1. Use the method shown above to solve each equation.

a.

see $\quad 5 \div \dfrac{1}{6} = \boxed{}$

think $\quad 5 \times (1 \div \dfrac{1}{6}) = \boxed{}$

b.

see $\quad 3 \div \dfrac{1}{8} = \boxed{}$

think $\quad 3 \times (1 \div \dfrac{1}{8}) = \boxed{}$

c.

see $\quad 7 \div \dfrac{1}{10} = \boxed{}$

think $\quad 7 \times (1 \div \dfrac{1}{10}) = \boxed{}$

d.

see $\quad 9 \div \dfrac{1}{5} = \boxed{}$

think $\quad 9 \times (1 \div \dfrac{1}{5}) = \boxed{}$

ORIGO Stepping Stones • Grade 5 • 9.3

© ORIGO Education

2. Use the method used in Question 1 to solve each equation.

a.
see  $6 \div \frac{1}{4} =$ ▢

think ▢ = ▢

b.
see $8 \div \frac{1}{5} =$ ▢

think ▢ = ▢

c.
see $10 \div \frac{1}{7} =$ ▢

think ▢ = ▢

d.
see $2 \div \frac{1}{9} =$ ▢

think ▢ = ▢

3. Solve each problem. Show your thinking.

a. Victor has 2 sheets of paper and splits each sheet into fifths. How many smaller pieces of paper does he have?

▢ smaller pieces

b. Layla has 6 meters of rope. She cuts it into shorter pieces that are each $\frac{1}{5}$ of a meter long. How many short pieces does she have?

▢ short pieces

Step Ahead   Complete each number trail. Use whole numbers where possible.

a. 8 → $\times \frac{1}{4}$ → ▢ → $\div \frac{1}{5}$ → ▢ → $\times \frac{1}{2}$ → ▢

b. 1 → $\div 4$ → ▢ → $\times \frac{1}{3}$ → ▢ → $\times 12$ → ▢

Common fractions: Solving word problems involving multiplication or division with a unit fraction

Step In

Look at these two word problems.

1 Three yards of ribbon are cut into half-yard lengths. How many pieces are cut?

2 Each large bow needs $\frac{1}{4}$ yd of ribbon. How much ribbon is needed to make 3 large bows?

How are they the same? How are they different?

The first problem starts with a total length that is split into equal lengths. That is division.

I could write a division equation, and then change it to a multiplication equation to find the answer.

$$3 \div \frac{1}{2} = ?$$  $$\boxed{} \times \frac{1}{2} = 3$$

The second problem is combining 3 equal lengths. That's multiplication.

$$3 \times \frac{1}{4} = \boxed{\frac{}{}}$$

Write the solution to each problem.

Step Up

1. Color the ○ to indicate if the problem is multiplication or division. Then calculate the answer. Show your thinking.

a. 2 yards of fabric is cut into strips that are each $\frac{1}{4}$ yd wide. How many strips are there?

○ Multiplication   ○ Division

$\boxed{}$ strips

b. The length of one side of a square picture frame is $\frac{1}{6}$ yd long. How much timber is needed for the whole picture frame?

○ Multiplication   ○ Division

$\boxed{\frac{}{}}$ yard

2. Write an equation to represent each problem. Use a letter to show the unknown amount. Then calculate each answer. Show your thinking.

a. 5 pounds of cooked rice was served in $\frac{1}{2}$-pound portions. How many portions of rice were served?

_____ portions

b. A muffin recipe requires $\frac{1}{3}$ of a cup of milk. How much milk is needed to make 5 batches?

cups

c. Cody broke a 1-mile run into 12 parts. In between the parts, he did 20 push-ups. What fraction of a mile did he run in each part?

mile

d. Some tasks that took $\frac{1}{4}$ of an hour each were done in 3 hours. What is the greatest number tasks that could be done in that time?

_____ tasks

Step Ahead

a. Write a word problem that matches this equation. $5 \div \frac{1}{3} = ?$

b. Exchange word problems with another student and write the answer to their problem below.

© ORIGO Education

Think and Solve

What is the two-digit mystery number? _____

- It is 1 more than a square number.
- It is 1 less than a multiple of 3.
- It is 2 more than a multiple of 4.
- The product of its digits is less than the sum of its digits.

Words at Work

Nancy used multiplication to solve this division problem. Explain her thinking in words.

$$7 \div \frac{1}{4} = \boxed{28}$$

$$? \times \frac{1}{4} = 7$$

$$? \times \frac{1}{4} = \frac{28}{4}$$

_____

_____

_____

_____

_____

_____

_____

_____

_____

_____

_____

_____

_____

_____

_____

Ongoing Practice

1. Estimate the difference in your head. Then use the standard algorithm to calculate the exact difference.

a.
9.73 kg   4.4 kg

b.
4.07 kg   11.28 kg

2. Compute the equations.

a.
see → $8 \div \frac{1}{6} = \boxed{}$

think → $\boxed{}$ = $\boxed{}$

b.
see → $7 \div \frac{1}{3} = \boxed{}$

think → $\boxed{}$ = $\boxed{}$

c.
see → $4 \div \frac{1}{5} = \boxed{}$

think → $\boxed{}$ = $\boxed{}$

d.
see → $6 \div \frac{1}{9} = \boxed{}$

think → $\boxed{}$ = $\boxed{}$

Preparing for Module 10

Each large square is one whole. Shade parts to show the decimal fraction. Then write the matching common fraction.

a.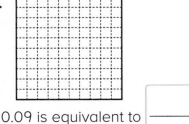

0.09 is equivalent to ⎯⎯

b.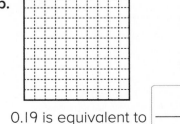

0.19 is equivalent to ⎯⎯

c.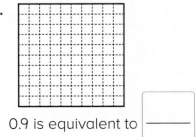

0.9 is equivalent to ⎯⎯

Step In

Four friends equally shared $\frac{1}{3}$ of a bowl of popcorn. What fraction of the original whole bowl did each friend eat?

Charlie drew a fraction strip to show his thinking.

What did he draw first?
What does it represent?

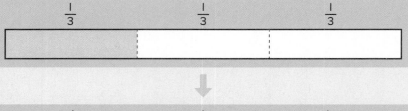

What did he draw next?

What does he need to do next to calculate how much each friend ate?

How does this finished diagram help Charlie find the answer?

I think he needs to figure out what fraction of the whole bowl the green part represents.

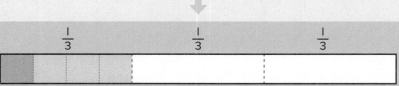

How could you use multiplication to check whether the quotient is correct?

Step Up

1. Read each story and write a division equation that shows what you need to calculate. Use a letter to show the unknown amount. You do not need to calculate the answer.

a. One-fifth of a block of cheese is sliced equally into 3 servings. What fraction of the whole block is in each share?

b. A team of 4 runners is competing in a relay that is $\frac{1}{4}$ of a mile. What fraction of a mile will each person run?

c. There is one-eighth of a gallon of milk. All the milk is poured equally into 2 glasses. What fraction of the milk is in each glass?

2. Solve each problem. Use the strips to help you complete each equation.

a. A pot of pasta was shared equally among 3 people. Teresa ate only half of her share. What fraction of the whole pot did she eat?

[   ]   [÷   =   ]

b. Four people ate one-third of an extra-large pizza. They each ate the same amount. What fraction of the whole pizza did each person eat?

[   ]   [÷   =   ]

3. Use multiplication to check these answers to division problems. Remember to use equivalent fractions.

a. $\dfrac{1}{3} \div 2 = \dfrac{1}{6}$

◯ Correct   ◯ Incorrect

b. $\dfrac{1}{2} \div 8 = \dfrac{1}{16}$

◯ Correct   ◯ Incorrect

c. $\dfrac{1}{5} \div 4 = \dfrac{1}{9}$

◯ Correct   ◯ Incorrect

d. $\dfrac{1}{7} \div 7 = \dfrac{1}{14}$

◯ Correct   ◯ Incorrect

Step Ahead

Complete this equation. Show your thinking. There is more than one possible answer.

$$\boxed{} \div \boxed{} = \dfrac{1}{24}$$

Step In

John noticed a pattern when dividing unit fractions by whole numbers.

What do you think he noticed?

$$\frac{1}{3} \div 5 = \frac{1}{15} \longrightarrow 3 \times 5 = 15$$

$$\frac{1}{4} \div 2 = \frac{1}{8} \longrightarrow 4 \times 2 = 8$$

$$\frac{1}{2} \div 6 = \frac{1}{12} \longrightarrow 2 \times 6 = 12$$

Mako was thinking about the same equations.

What do you think she noticed? What operation does the word **of** indicate?

$$\frac{1}{3} \div 5 = \frac{1}{15} \longrightarrow \frac{1}{5} \text{ of } \frac{1}{3} = \frac{1}{15}$$

$$\frac{1}{4} \div 2 = \frac{1}{8} \longrightarrow \frac{1}{2} \text{ of } \frac{1}{4} = \frac{1}{8}$$

$$\frac{1}{2} \div 6 = \frac{1}{12} \longrightarrow \frac{1}{6} \text{ of } \frac{1}{2} = \frac{1}{12}$$

Dividing by a whole number is the same as multiplying by a unit fraction. I think it will be easier to multiply two common fractions than divide a fraction by a whole number.

Step Up

1. Write each division expression as a multiplication expression.

a. $\frac{1}{3} \div 2$

is equivalent to

⬚⁄⬚ of ⬚

⬚⁄⬚ × ⬚

b. $\frac{1}{2} \div 4$

is equivalent to

⬚⁄⬚ of ⬚

⬚⁄⬚ × ⬚

c. $6 \div 5$

is equivalent to

⬚⁄⬚ of ⬚

⬚⁄⬚ × ⬚

d. $4 \div 7$

is equivalent to

⬚⁄⬚ of ⬚

⬚⁄⬚ × ⬚

e. $7 \div 9$

is equivalent to

⬚⁄⬚ of ⬚

⬚⁄⬚ × ⬚

f. $12 \div 5$

is equivalent to

⬚⁄⬚ of ⬚

⬚⁄⬚ × ⬚

g. $\frac{1}{8} \div 3$

is equivalent to

⬚⁄⬚ of ⬚

⬚⁄⬚ × ⬚

h. $1 \div 2$

is equivalent to

⬚⁄⬚ of ⬚

⬚⁄⬚ × ⬚

2. Read each problem. Write a division expression, then a matching multiplication expression. Then write the answer.

a. 4 people equally share half a bowl of dip. What fraction of the whole bowl do they each eat?

☐ ÷ ☐   ☐ × ☐   ☐/☐ of the bowl

b. A pitcher of punch is $\frac{1}{3}$ full. 5 people share the punch equally. How much of the remaining punch do they each get?

☐ ÷ ☐   ☐ × ☐   ☐/☐ of the punch

c. A new swimming pool is $\frac{1}{5}$ full. It took 3 hours to fill it that much. How full was it after one hour?

☐ ÷ ☐   ☐ × ☐   ☐/☐ full

d. A $\frac{1}{2}$ lb of grapes is shared evenly among 3 people. What fraction of the half pound does each person eat?

☐ ÷ ☐   ☐ × ☐   ☐/☐ of a half pound

3. Solve each equation. Show your thinking.

a.
$4 \times (\frac{1}{5} \div 6) =$ ☐

b.
$7 - \frac{1}{3} \div 8 =$ ☐

4. Write an equation to match the sentence. Use a letter for the unknown amount.

a. Divide $\frac{1}{3}$ by 6, then multiply by 2.

b. Add 5 and $\frac{1}{9}$, then divide the result by 4.

Step Ahead

Rewrite these equations using what you know about division with fractions. Then calculate the answers.

a.
$7 \div 3 \div 5 \div 8 =$ ☐

b.
$\frac{1}{3} \div 5 \times \frac{1}{4} \div 6 =$ ☐

Computation Practice

★ Use a ruler to draw a line to the correct product. The line will pass through a number and a letter. Write each letter above its matching number at the bottom of the page to discover a fact about the natural world. Some letters appear more than once.

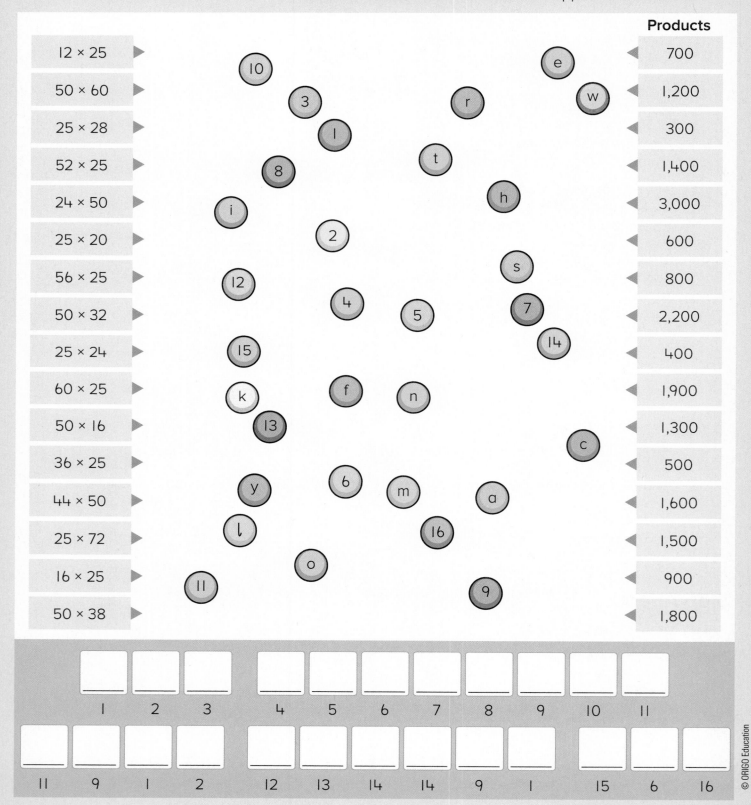

12 × 25 ▶			**Products**
50 × 60 ▶			◀ 700
25 × 28 ▶			◀ 1,200
52 × 25 ▶			◀ 300
24 × 50 ▶			◀ 1,400
25 × 20 ▶			◀ 3,000
56 × 25 ▶			◀ 600
50 × 32 ▶			◀ 800
25 × 24 ▶			◀ 2,200
60 × 25 ▶			◀ 400
50 × 16 ▶			◀ 1,900
36 × 25 ▶			◀ 1,300
44 × 50 ▶			◀ 500
25 × 72 ▶			◀ 1,600
16 × 25 ▶			◀ 1,500
50 × 38 ▶			◀ 900
			◀ 1,800

Bottom answer boxes:

1	2	3	4	5	6	7	8	9	10	11

11	9	1	2	12	13	14	14	9	1	15	6	16

ORIGO Stepping Stones · Grade 5 · 9.6

Ongoing Practice

1. Calculate each difference. Show your thinking.

a.
$13.05 - 4.18 =$ _____

b.
$9.2 - 5.36 =$ _____

c.
$8.75 - 6.81 =$ _____

2. For each of these, write the multiplication equation that matches. Then write the answers.

a.
$\frac{1}{5} \div 8 =$ ____

____ × ____ = ____

b.
$\frac{1}{3} \div 4 =$ ____

____ × ____ = ____

c.
$\frac{1}{6} \div 7 =$ ____

____ × ____ = ____

d.
$\frac{1}{8} \div 5 =$ ____

____ × ____ = ____

e.
$\frac{1}{7} \div 4 =$ ____

____ × ____ = ____

f.
$\frac{1}{4} \div 9 =$ ____

____ × ____ = ____

Preparing for Module 10

Write each partial product. Then add them to find the total.

a. 4×48

4 | [40 | 8]

$4 \times$ _____ = _____

$4 \times$ _____ = _____

Total _____

b. 7×36

7 | [30 | 6]

$7 \times$ _____ = _____

$7 \times$ _____ = _____

Total _____

Step In   Look at these two word problems.

1 Leila cuts $\frac{1}{2}$ yd of lumber into 3 equal lengths. How long is each piece?

$\frac{1}{2}$ yd

2 How many half-yard lengths of lumber can be cut from a piece that is 3 yards long?

3 yd

| $\frac{1}{2}$ yd | $\frac{1}{2}$ yd | $\frac{1}{2}$ yd | $\frac{1}{2}$ yd | $\frac{1}{2}$ yd | $\frac{1}{2}$ yd |

How are they the same? How are they different?

Both problems sound like division.

The first problem is like sharing among 3.

The second problem is finding the number of halves in 3, so each of these equations should match one of the problems.

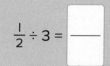

$\frac{1}{2} \div 3 = \dfrac{}{}$

$3 \div \frac{1}{2} = \boxed{}$

How would you solve each problem? Complete each equation.

Remember, when you divide sometimes you can *think multiplication* to help.

Step Up   1.   Solve each problem. Show your thinking.

a. At a steady pace, it takes $\frac{1}{4}$ hour to walk one kilometer. How far could you walk in 3 hours if you keep the same pace?

_____ km

b. A fast athlete can run 3 kilometers in $\frac{1}{4}$ of an hour. How long does it take the athlete to run one kilometer?

hr

2. Write an equation to represent each problem. Use a letter to show the unknown amount. Then calculate the answers. Show your thinking.

a. A granola recipe requires $\frac{1}{3}$ of a cup of raisins. How many batches can be made with 3 cups of raisins?

_____ = _____

[ ] batches

b. Thomas's shirt costs $8, which is $\frac{1}{6}$ of the price of Ruby's shirt. How much does Ruby's shirt cost?

_____ = _____

$ [ ]

c. Juan scores 8 goals in $\frac{1}{4}$ hour. Kayla scores 24 in the same time. How many times greater is Kayla's score than Juan's score?

_____ = _____

[ ] times

d. An assembly line produces a new car every 6 minutes. What fraction of an hour is 6 minutes? How many cars are produced in 8 hours?

_____ = _____

6 minutes is [ ] hour

[ ] cars are produced in 8 hours

Step Ahead

Kevin can wrap 4 bunches of flowers every $\frac{1}{4}$ hour. Laura can wrap 5 bunches every $\frac{1}{3}$ of an hour. Complete this table to compare the number of bunches each person wraps in 1, 2, 4, 6, and 8 hours.

Hours	1 hour	2 hours	4 hours	6 hours	8 hours
Kevin					
Laura					

Step In

This number line represents one meter.

0

Write a number at the right-hand end to mark the line in centimeters.

Write another number at the right-hand end to mark the line in millimeters.

Where would you draw a mark to show the length that is 50 cm long?
Use your ruler to determine the halfway mark and label the point.

What are all the different ways you could describe and write that length?

You could describe the length in millimeters, and as a fraction of a meter, which could be written as a decimal fraction or common fraction.

Think about the relationship between each metric unit. Then write the missing length.

| _____ meter | is equivalent to | 150 centimeters | is equivalent to | 1,500 millimeters |

What do you know about kilometers? How many meters are equivalent to one kilometer?

Step Up

1. Measure each strip. Write the length in millimeters, then as a decimal fraction of a meter.

a.

_____ mm   _____ m

b.

_____ mm   _____ m

c.

_____ mm   _____ m

2. Write equivalent lengths.

a.

_____ m $3\frac{2}{10}$ m _____ cm _____ mm

b.

_____ m _____ m 425 cm _____ mm

c.

_____ m _____ m _____ cm 6,540 mm

d.

_____ m $\frac{67}{1000}$ m _____ cm _____ mm

3. Write each length as a decimal fraction, then as a mixed number.

a. 3,650 m	**b.** 2,780 m	**c.** 4,190 m	**d.** 1,325 m
_____ km	_____ km	_____ km	_____ km
_____ km	_____ km	_____ km	_____ km

Step Ahead   Choose the number that makes the most sense to complete the sentence.

a.

The book is _____ m thick.

b.

Cody can stand and leap _____ cm.

Think and Solve

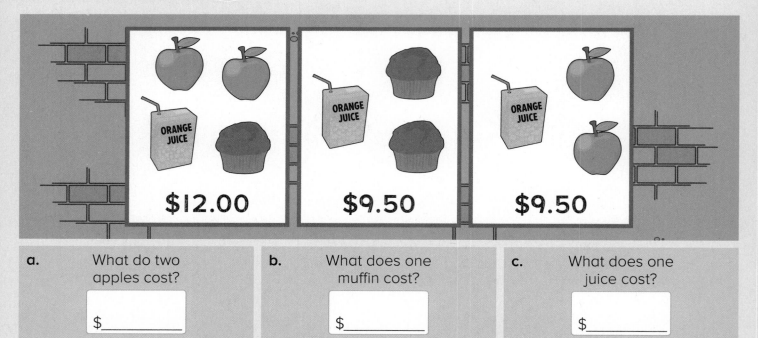

$12.00 $9.50 $9.50

a. What do two apples cost?

$_____

b. What does one muffin cost?

$_____

c. What does one juice cost?

$_____

Words at Work

Write a word problem that involves multiplication or division with a unit fraction. Then write the answer.

_____
_____
_____
_____
_____
_____
_____
_____
_____
_____

Ongoing Practice

FROM 5.5.9

1. Calculate the difference in height between these amusement park rides. Show your thinking.

a.	Giant Drop	40.15 meters
	Roller Coaster	6.71 meters

_____ m

b.	Whiplash	13.82 meters
	Terrifying Tower	61.95 meters

_____ m

2. Write each length as a decimal fraction, then as a mixed number.

FROM 5.9.8

a.	4,355 m	b.	2,350 m	c.	3,465 m	d.	5,295 m

_____ km

_____ km

_____ km

_____ km

_____ km

_____ km

_____ km

_____ km

Preparing for Module 10

Write a multiplication equation to show each part.
Then write the total of the four partial products.

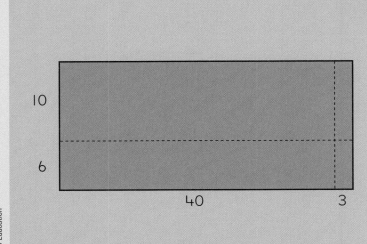

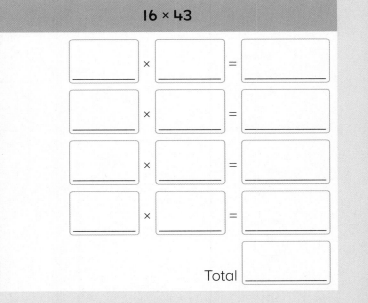

16 × 43

_____ × _____ = _____

_____ × _____ = _____

_____ × _____ = _____

_____ × _____ = _____

Total _____

Step In

How could you label the marks on this scale?

Could your label be written in more than one way?
How do you know?

The marks between 0 kg and 1 kg can be a number of grams or a fraction of a kilogram.

How many grams are equivalent to one kilogram?

Show the position of each mass below on the scale.

| 700 g | 1.2 kg | $1\frac{4}{10}$ kg | $\frac{3}{4}$ kg |

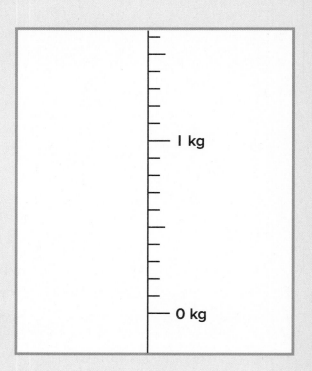

Step Up

1. Write each mass in kilograms and in grams.

A   _____ kg = _____ g

B   _____ kg = _____ g

C   _____ kg = _____ g

D   _____ kg = _____ g

E   _____ kg = _____ g

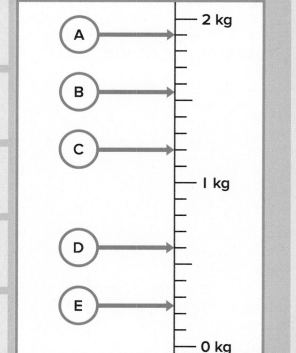

2. Write numbers to show equivalent masses. Use decimal fractions and mixed numbers where necessary.

a.

4,300 g = [_____] kg = [_____] kg

b.

[_____] g = 1.8 kg = [_____] kg

c.

[_____] g = [_____] kg = $2\frac{1}{2}$ kg

d.

6,750 g = [_____] kg = [_____] kg

e.

90 g = [_____] kg = [_____] kg

f.

[_____] g = [_____] kg = $\frac{450}{1000}$ kg

3. Solve each problem. Show your thinking.

a. Andrew packed seven 200 g boxes and five 150 g boxes together. What was the total mass of the package?

[_____] kg

b. A box of pasta weighs exactly 1 kg. Each pack inside the box weighs 50 g. How many packs of pasta are in 2 boxes?

[_____] packs

Step Ahead Write these masses in order from **least** to **greatest**.

a.

| 8.1 kg | 81 g | 8.15 kg | 810 g | 8,000 g |

[_____] [_____] [_____] [_____] [_____]

b.

| 3.75 kg | 375 g | 0.370 kg | 3,705 g | 37.5 kg |

[_____] [_____] [_____] [_____] [_____]

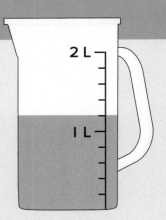

Step In

How much juice is in this pitcher?

Imagine the juice was poured into containers that each held 200 mL.
How many of the smaller containers could you fill?
How many milliliters are in one liter?

Complete these statements.

	mL	is equivalent to	1 liter	
	mL	is equivalent to	$\frac{1}{10}$ liter **or**	0.1 liter
	mL	is equivalent to	$\frac{1}{2}$ liter **or**	0.5 liter
	mL	is equivalent to	$\frac{1}{4}$ liter **or**	0.25 liter

Step Up

1. Look carefully at each scale. Then write the amount in each container three different ways.

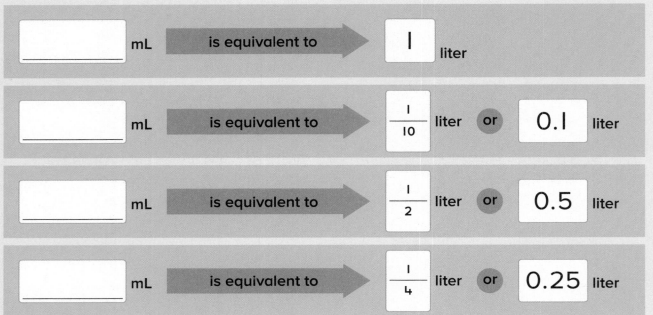

Whole number	mL	mL	mL
Common fraction	L	L	L
Decimal fraction	L	L	L

2. Color the three labels that match each amount.

a.

2.5 L
250 mL
$\frac{1}{4}$ L
0.25 L

b.

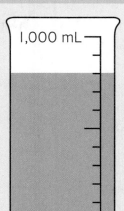

0.8 L
$\frac{8}{10}$ L
800 mL
8,000 mL

c.

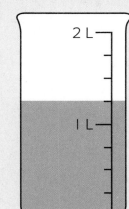

$1\frac{1}{4}$ L
1.25 L
1,250 mL
125 mL

d.

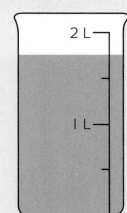

750 mL
1.75 L
1,750 mL
$1\frac{3}{4}$ L

Step Ahead

Write two ways you could fill this container to the 2 L mark using these two measuring cups.

150 mL

250 mL

Method A

Method B

Computation Practice

⭐ Complete the equations. Then write each letter above its matching answer at the bottom of the page to discover a fact about history. Some letters appear more than once.

16.2 + 9 = _____ **i**

19 − 16.7 = _____ **a**

3.7 + 24.7 = _____ **o**

23.1 − 16.2 = _____ **n**

0.7 + 29.6 = _____ **j**

15 − 7.2 = _____ **r**

25.8 + 0.9 = _____ **m**

34.5 − 7 = _____ **h**

17.8 + 5.4 = _____ **f**

12.4 + 0.7 = _____ **y**

4.9 + 10.5 = _____ **w**

18.8 − 8.3 = _____ **t**

8.3 + 18.8 = _____ **s**

21.7 − 2.8 = _____ **e**

12 + 9.8 = _____ **p**

30.2 − 1.5 = _____ **d**

20.4 + 10.7 = _____ **b**

30.4 − 0.8 = _____ **l**

59.1 + 1.2 = _____ **c**

| 30.3 | 25.2 | 26.7 | 26.7 | 13.1 | | 60.3 | 2.3 | 7.8 | 10.5 | 18.9 | 7.8 |

| 15.4 | 2.3 | 27.1 | | 10.5 | 27.5 | 18.9 | | 23.2 | 25.2 | 7.8 | 27.1 | 10.5 |

| 21.8 | 7.8 | 18.9 | 27.1 | 25.2 | 28.7 | 18.9 | 6.9 | 10.5 | | 31.1 | 28.4 | 7.8 | 6.9 |

| 25.2 | 6.9 | | 2.3 |

| 27.5 | 28.4 | 27.1 | 21.8 | 25.2 | 10.5 | 2.3 | 29.6 |

Ongoing Practice

I. Solve each problem. Show your thinking.

a. Red markers are sold in packs of 8. There are 3,702 markers. How many full packs can be made?

_____ packs

b. Oranges are packed in 5 kilogram bags. There are 6,027 kg of oranges to pack. How many bags can be packed?

_____ bags

2. Convert these lengths.

a. _____ m = 380 mm

b. 265 mm = _____ m

c. _____ cm = 90 mm

d. 72 cm = _____ m

e. _____ m = 128 cm

f. 138.1 cm = _____ mm

g. _____ cm = 85 mm

h. 46.2 cm = _____ m

Preparing for Module 10

Think multiplication to calculate the missing dimension. Write the equations to match.

a.

7 m   Area = 56 m²

_____ m

□ × □ = □

□ ÷ □ = □

b.

Area = 32 in²   _____ in

8 in

□ × □ = □

□ ÷ □ = □

Step In
Read each of these problems.

a. Nathan has to fence a large rectangular field. The longer side of the field is 1.6 km, which is twice the length of the shorter side. He has 5,000 m of fencing.

How many meters of fencing will he have left over?

b. Three packages are each filled with 400 g boxes. Each package weighs 2 kg.

How many 400 g boxes were used?

c. Rozene drew a chart with 5 columns. Three columns were 35 mm wide and 2 columns were 5 cm wide.

How wide was the finished chart?

d. Oscar buys 2 L of juice and six 375 mL cans of soda water. He pours the juice and soda into one large bowl to make punch.

How much punch did he make?

Which problems are about length?

What measurement attribute are the other problems about?

Look carefully at problem a.
What steps would you follow to solve this problem?

I would convert the length of the longer side into meters to help calculate the perimeter.

How would you solve each of the other problems?

Step Up
1. Solve each problem. Show your thinking.

a. Sheree pours 2 L of water equally into 10 cups. Each cup can hold 400 mL. There is no water left in the bottle. How much water is in each cup?

_____ mL

b. A customer orders 8 bags of rice that each weigh $\frac{1}{2}$ kg, and 12 packets of popcorn that each weigh 150 g. What is the total mass of the order?

_____ kg

2. Solve each problem. Show your thinking.

a. Carlos has a tub that can hold $2\frac{1}{4}$ L, which is a third of what Corey's container can hold. Corey's container is half full of water. How much water does he have?

_____ mL

b. Nicole has a 10 m ball of string. She cuts 6 lengths of 40 cm each, and 5 lengths at 600 mm each. How much string does she use?

_____ cm

c. Dixon is running a 5 km fun run. He runs 1,500 m to checkpoint 1, then $1\frac{3}{4}$ km to checkpoint 2. How many more meters does he have left to run?

_____ m

d. Stella makes $1\frac{1}{2}$ kg of burger patties. She places the patties in rows of 5 on a tray. Each patty weighs about 100 g. How many rows are there?

_____ rows

Step Ahead   Circle the special that you think is the better buy. Explain your thinking.

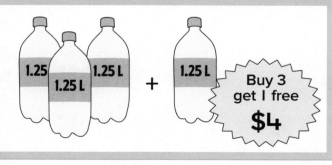

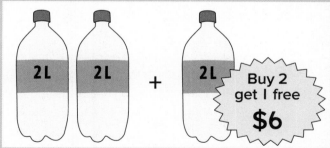

_____

_____

_____

Step In   A farmer has weighed some of his pumpkin crop.

The mass of each pumpkin has been rounded to the nearest one-half of a kilogram.
This line plot shows the mass of the pumpkins.

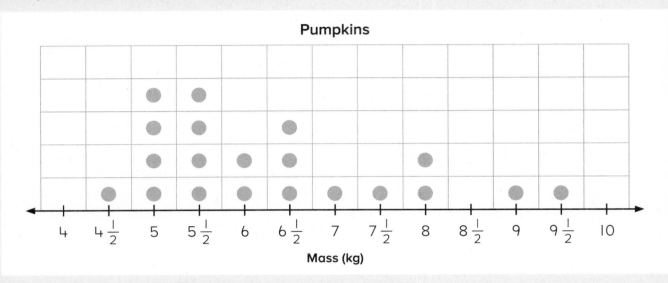

What does the line plot tell you about the mass of the pumpkins?

How many pumpkins did the farmer weigh?

What is the difference in mass between the lightest and heaviest pumpkins?

How many pumpkins are heavier than $6\frac{1}{2}$ kg?

How many pumpkins are lighter than 7 kg?

The pumpkins in last season's crop weighed about $5\frac{1}{2}$ kg each.

Are the pumpkins in this season's crop heavier or lighter?
How do you know?

Step Up   Another farmer weighed 20 pumpkins. Each mass is recorded below.
Use this data to complete the line plot on page 353. You will need to convert
the grams to kilograms.

6 kg	$9\frac{1}{2}$ kg	5 kg	5 kg	6,500 g
5,500 g	4 kg	$5\frac{1}{2}$ kg	$9\frac{1}{2}$ kg	7 kg
$4\frac{1}{2}$ kg	8 kg	5,000 g	$6\frac{1}{2}$ kg	$5\frac{1}{2}$ kg
4,500 g	9,000 g	$5\frac{1}{2}$ kg	$4\frac{1}{2}$ kg	$5\frac{1}{2}$ kg

1. Draw to represent each mass shown at the bottom of page 352.

Pumpkins

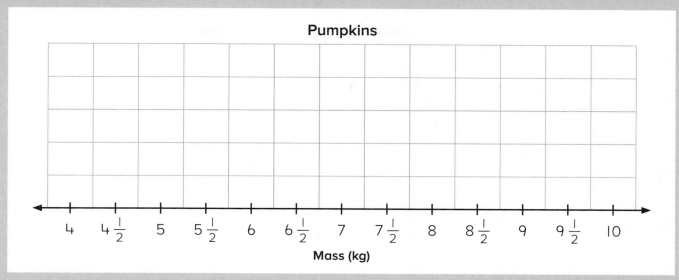

Mass (kg)

2. Look at the line plot above.

   a. Which mass was recorded most often? ☐ kg

   b. How many pumpkins weighed **exactly** $6\frac{1}{2}$ kg? ☐

   c. How many pumpkins were **heavier** than 5 kg? ☐

   d. What is the difference in mass between the lightest and heaviest pumpkins? ☐ kg

3. Use the line plot above to solve each problem. Show your thinking on page 356.

   a. The pumpkins that weigh more than $5\frac{1}{2}$ kg are put together in a box to sell. What is the total mass of these pumpkins? _____ kg

   b. What is the total mass of the pumpkins that are equal to or less than $5\frac{1}{2}$ kg? _____ kg

Step Ahead

Compare the line plots on pages 352 and 353. Which line plot shows the heavier crop of pumpkins? Explain your thinking.

Think and Solve

The numbers in the circles are the sums of the rows and the columns. Same letters are the same numbers.

D	C	A	(21.1)
C	A	B	(15.9)
D	C	A	(21.1)
C	D	B	(20.4)

(35.2) (30.7) (12.6)

A = _____   B = _____   C = _____   D = _____

Words at Work

Write words to make true sentences involving length, mass, and capacity.

a. One-fourth of a _____ is equivalent to 250 _____.

b. _____ millimeters is equivalent to six _____.

c. One thousand _____ is equivalent to one _____.

d. One thousand _____ is equivalent to one _____.

e. One-half of a _____ is equivalent to 500 milliters.

f. The abbreviation for milliliter is _____.

g. One thousand _____ fifty milliliters is equivalent to one and one-fourth liters.

© ORIGO Education

Ongoing Practice

1. Solve each problem. Show your thinking.

a. There are 12 vanilla beans in each bag. 6,048 vanilla beans have been picked. How many bags can be filled?

_____ bags

b. Each necklace needs 20 beads. There are 4,520 beads. How many necklaces can be made?

_____ necklaces

2. Solve each problem. Show your thinking and be sure to use the correct units in your answer.

a. A plumber needs 3 meters of pipe. He connects one length of 156 cm and another that is 2,050 mm. What is the combined length?

_____ cm

b. Archie rides $1\frac{3}{4}$ km to the store, another 400 m to the park, then $1\frac{1}{4}$ km home. How far does he ride?

_____ m

Preparing for Module 10

Complete the equations.

a.

see ➤ $4 \div \frac{1}{8} = \boxed{}$

think ➤ [_____] = [____]

b.

see ➤ $3 \div \frac{1}{6} = \boxed{}$

think ➤ [_____] = [____]

Step In

Each square represents one whole.

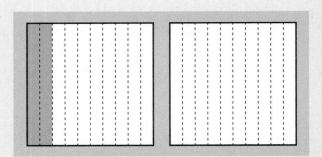

The shaded part shows one group of 0.2.

How could you show 4 groups of 0.2?
What about 6 × 0.2?

This number line is used to calculate 6 × 0.05.

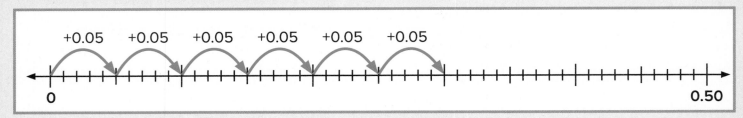

+0.05 +0.05 +0.05 +0.05 +0.05 +0.05

0   0.50

What steps are followed?

How could you use the same number line to calculate 9 × 0.04?

Lifen knows that 9 × 4 = 36.
She records the product on a place-value slider.

H	T	O	.	t	h
	3	6	.		

How can she adjust the slider to calculate 9 × 0.4?
What about 9 × 0.04?

What happens as the
factor decreases in value?

If I divide my factor by 10, my answer
will be divided by 10, so the digits
move one place to the right.

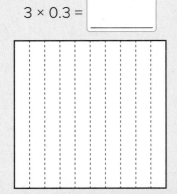

Step Up

1. Write the products. Color or outline parts of the squares to show your thinking.

a.
3 × 0.2 = _____

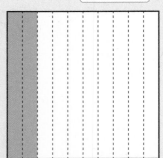

b.
2 × 0.4 = _____

c.
3 × 0.3 = _____

2. Complete these equations. Draw jumps on the number line to show your thinking.

a.

$5 \times 0.05 = $ ☐

0   0.50

b.

$3 \times 0.07 = $ ☐

0   0.50

c.

$5 \times 0.06 = $ ☐

0   0.50

d.

$3 \times 0.09 = $ ☐

0   0.50

3. Complete these equations.

a.

$3 \times 4 = $ ☐

$3 \times 0.4 = $ ☐

$3 \times 0.04 = $ ☐

b.

$8 \times 3 = $ ☐

$8 \times 0.3 = $ ☐

$8 \times 0.03 = $ ☐

c.

$9 \times 7 = $ ☐

$9 \times 0.7 = $ ☐

$9 \times 0.07 = $ ☐

4. Look at the equations in Question 3. Describe a pattern you see.

Step Ahead

Anya knows $6 \times 8 = 48$.
How could she use this fact to calculate 6×0.08?

Step In

Each square represents one whole.

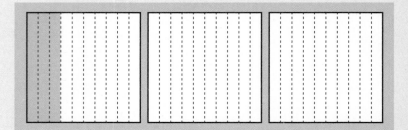

Color more parts to calculate 9×0.3.

What is the product?
How would you calculate the same product on a number line?

What is another way to calculate the product?

Anna uses a known multiplication fact.

> I know $9 \times 3 = 27$.
> Multiplying by 0.3 will give a product one-tenth of 9×3, so 9×0.3 must be 2.7

Henry uses place-value language.

> 9×0.3 is equivalent to 9×3 tenths, which is 27 tenths.
> 27 tenths equals 2 wholes and 7 tenths

Chloe figures it out like this.

> 9×0.3 is equivalent to
> $\frac{9}{1} \times \frac{3}{10} = \frac{27}{10}$
> $\frac{27}{10} = 2\frac{7}{10} = 2.7$

What steps do they each follow?
How are Henry's and Chloe's steps similar? How are they different?

Which method would you use to solve 7×0.6?

If the problem was 0.6×7 instead of 7×0.6, would it change your thinking about how to solve it?

Step Up

1. Use a known multiplication fact to help multiply each decimal fraction. Use the picture of the place-value slider to help your thinking.

a.

$6 \times 8 = 48$

6×0.08 is one-hundredth of 6×8 so

$6 \times 0.08 = \boxed{}$

b.
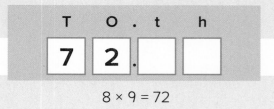

$8 \times 9 = 72$

8×0.9 is one-tenth of 8×9 so

$8 \times 0.9 = \boxed{}$

2. Rewrite each equation with common fractions. Then calculate the product.

a. $6 \times 0.4 = \underline{\hspace{3cm}}$

b. $5 \times 0.07 = \underline{\hspace{3cm}}$

c. $0.02 \times 7 = \underline{\hspace{3cm}}$

d. $0.6 \times 6 = \underline{\hspace{3cm}}$

e. $4 \times 0.8 = \underline{\hspace{3cm}}$

f. $0.09 \times 1 = \underline{\hspace{3cm}}$

3. Use a method of your choice to multiply each decimal fraction. Show your thinking.

a. $5 \times 0.3 = \underline{\hspace{2cm}}$

b. $0.04 \times 7 = \underline{\hspace{2cm}}$

c. $0.08 \times 8 = \underline{\hspace{2cm}}$

d. $1 \times 0.6 = \underline{\hspace{2cm}}$

e. $9 \times 0.05 = \underline{\hspace{2cm}}$

f. $0 \times 0.7 = \underline{\hspace{2cm}}$

4. Complete each equation.

a. $3 \times 0.6 = \underline{\hspace{2cm}}$

b. $\underline{\hspace{2cm}} = 5 \times 0.04$

c. $\underline{\hspace{2cm}} \times 0.3 = 2.4$

Step Ahead

Hernando knows that $7 \times 9 = 63$. How can he use this multiplication fact to calculate 7×0.9? Explain your thinking

Computation Practice

Throw me off the tallest building and I will not break, but put me in the ocean and I will. What am I?

★ Complete the equations. Then find each quotient in the puzzle below and shade the matching letter. The remaining letters will spell the answer.

$524 \div 4 =$ _____

$345 \div 5 =$ _____

$528 \div 3 =$ _____

$396 \div 4 =$ _____

$275 \div 5 =$ _____

$243 \div 3 =$ _____

$516 \div 4 =$ _____

$423 \div 3 =$ _____

$656 \div 4 =$ _____

$485 \div 5 =$ _____

$384 \div 3 =$ _____

$264 \div 4 =$ _____

$395 \div 5 =$ _____

$534 \div 3 =$ _____

$695 \div 5 =$ _____

$276 \div 3 =$ _____

$472 \div 4 =$ _____

$565 \div 5 =$ _____

$441 \div 3 =$ _____

$192 \div 4 =$ _____

$785 \div 5 =$ _____

© ORIGO Education

Ongoing Practice

1. Round the consumption figure for each country to the nearest pound.
Complete the bar graph to show the data.

Consumption of Beef by Each Person in One Year	
Country	Number of pounds
U.S.A	53.84
Brazil	60.4
Argentina	96.95
Australia	49.64

Title: _____

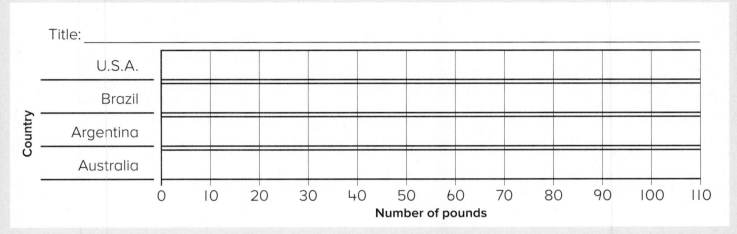

Country (axis)

U.S.A. / Brazil / Argentina / Australia

0 10 20 30 40 50 60 70 80 90 100 110
Number of pounds

2. Complete these equations. Draw jumps on the number line to show your thinking.

a.

$6 \times 0.08 =$ ☐

0 ——————————— 0.50

b.

$4 \times 0.09 =$ ☐

0 ——————————— 0.50

c.

$5 \times 0.07 =$ ☐

0 ——————————— 0.50

Preparing for Module 11

Read the rule. Complete the table.

			Number of tickets × 3 = Total cost			
Number of tickets	1	2	3	5	10	15
Total cost ($)						

Step In

Use the length of your hand to estimate the dimensions of this poster.

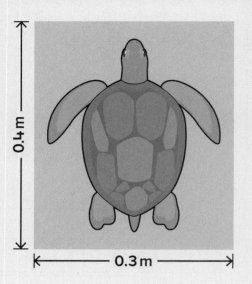

Do you think the area of the poster is more or less than one square meter? Explain your thinking.

How could you calculate the exact area? What equivalent expression could you write?

I would use common fractions and think $\frac{4}{10} \times \frac{3}{10}$.

This is a picture of a larger square that has an area of one square meter.

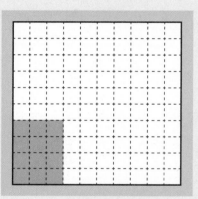

Eva shaded parts of the square to match the dimensions of the turtle poster above.

What is the area of the poster? How do you know?

Step Up

1. Each large square represents one whole. Label the dimensions on the square. Shade the area, then write the product.

a.
$0.4 \times 0.2 = \underline{\hspace{2cm}}$

b.
$0.2 \times 0.3 = \underline{\hspace{2cm}}$

c.
$0.9 \times 0.1 = \underline{\hspace{2cm}}$

2. Shade the square to match the dimensions. Then write the product.

a.
$0.5 \times 0.3 = $ ____

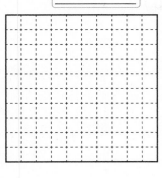

b.
$0.4 \times 0.5 = $ ____

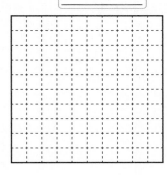

c.
$0.6 \times 0.8 = $ ____

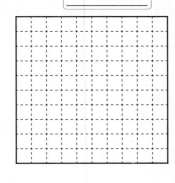

3. Complete each equation.

a.
$0.4 \times 0.8 = $ ____

b.
____ $\times 0.5 = 0.35$

c.
$4.2 = $ ____ $\times 0.7$

d.
____ $\times 0.9 = 0.45$

e.
$0.9 \times 5 = $ ____

f.
____ $\times 0.8 = 0.72$

g.
$0.32 = $ ____ $\times 0.8$

h.
$8 \times 0.3 = $ ____

i.
$0.06 = 0.6 \times $ ____

Step Ahead

Imagine you take one ball from each jar. Use the digits shown on those balls to complete this expression.

0.____ $\times$ 0.____

Is it ever possible to have a product equal to or greater than one? ____

Explain your thinking.

_____

_____

_____

Step In

A leftover roll of carpet is 5 m long and 0.42 m wide.
Marvin is thinking of using it to carpet his daughter's playhouse.

What floor area do you think the leftover carpet will cover?

> The carpet would cover 5 square meters if it were I m wide. The carpet is a little less than $\frac{1}{2}$ that width, so it will cover half as much.

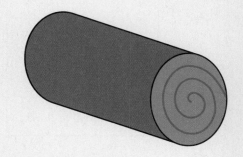

Lomasi draws this picture to calculate the area that it would cover.

How does she split the width of the carpet into parts that are easier to multiply?

Complete these equations to calculate each partial product.

$5 \times 0.4 = $ ☐

$5 \times 0.02 = $ ☐

> I've used this strategy before to multiply whole numbers.

What area can the leftover carpet cover?

How would you use this strategy to calculate 6 × 0.36?

Step Up

1. Calculate the partial products. Then write the total.

a.

$8 \times 0.32 = $ ☐

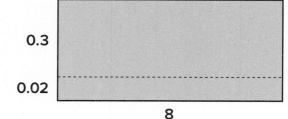

$8 \times 0.3 = $ ☐ $8 \times 0.02 = $ ☐

b.

$7 \times 0.65 = $ ☐

$7 \times 0.6 = $ ☐ $7 \times 0.05 = $ ☐

2. Calculate each partial product. Then write the total.

a.

$3 \times 0.23 =$ _____

$3 \times 0.2 =$ _____

$3 \times 0.03 =$ _____

b.

$5 \times 0.15 =$ _____

$5 \times 0.1 =$ _____

$5 \times 0.05 =$ _____

c.

$3 \times 0.19 =$ _____

$3 \times 0.1 =$ _____

$3 \times 0.09 =$ _____

3. Calculate each product. Show your thinking.

a.

$5 \times 0.37 =$ _____

b.

$0.42 \times 4 =$ _____

c.

$3 \times 0.49 =$ _____

4. Solve each problem. Show your thinking.

a. Brianna has 5 water bottles to fill. Each bottle holds 0.45 L. How much water will she use to fill 3 of them?

_____ L

b. Deon's shirt is 4 times larger than Helen's, but costs half as much. Deon's shirt costs $9.35. How much is Helen's shirt?

$ _____

Step Ahead Look at this calculation. Describe the mistake in words. Then write the correct product below.

🔍 $5 \times 0.39 = 0.60$

$5 \times 0.3 = 0.15$
$5 \times 0.09 = 0.45$

_____

Think and Solve

Look at this grid of numbers.

14	23	17	9
12	13	28	4
6	13	10	19
15	11	16	18
5	8	2	7

Change the positions of 2 pairs of numbers in the grid so the sum of every row and column is a multiple of 10. Write the numbers in this empty grid and circle the numbers you changed.

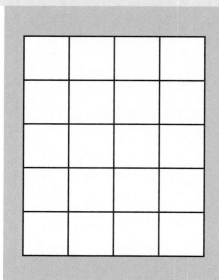

Words at Work

Explain in words three different methods you could use to calculate 7 × 0.09. Include the solution.

1. Most watermelons weigh about 20 pounds. A farmer is testing a new variety of fertilizer to see if it increases the mass of watermelons. This line plot shows the mass of the watermelons from the test.

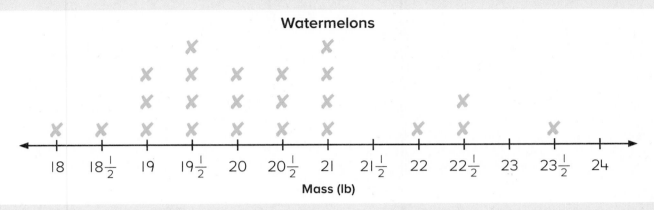

Watermelons

Mass (lb)

What does the line plot tell you about the new fertilizer the farmer used?

2. Rewrite each equation with common fractions. Then calculate the product.

a.
5 × 0.5 = _____

b.
6 × 0.03 = _____

c.
0.04 × 9 = _____

Preparing for Module 11   Solve this problem. Complete the table to help you.

Two boxes hold 50 packets of pins, 4 boxes hold 100 packets of pins, and 6 boxes hold 150 packets of pins. How many packets of pins are in 9 boxes?

Boxes					
Packets					

_____ packets

FROM 5.4.12

FROM 5.10.2

© ORIGO Education

Step In

Brady uses the partial-products strategy to solve two separate equations.

He draws these two pictures to help.

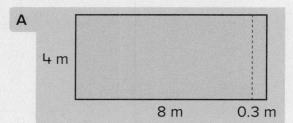

A — 4 m, 8 m, 0.3 m

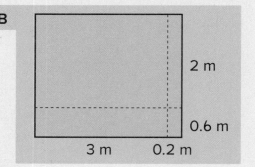

B — 2 m, 0.6 m, 3 m, 0.2 m

Write the side lengths that you think he was trying to multiply.

A [ ] × [ ]

B [ ] × [ ]

How would you calculate the product for Example A? What partial products would you add?

How many partial products must you add to solve Example B? What is the total product?

How could you use the same thinking to calculate 5.1 × 8.25?

Each example splits the decimal fractions into parts that are easier to multiply.

Step Up

Use this apartment floor plan to answer the questions on page 371.

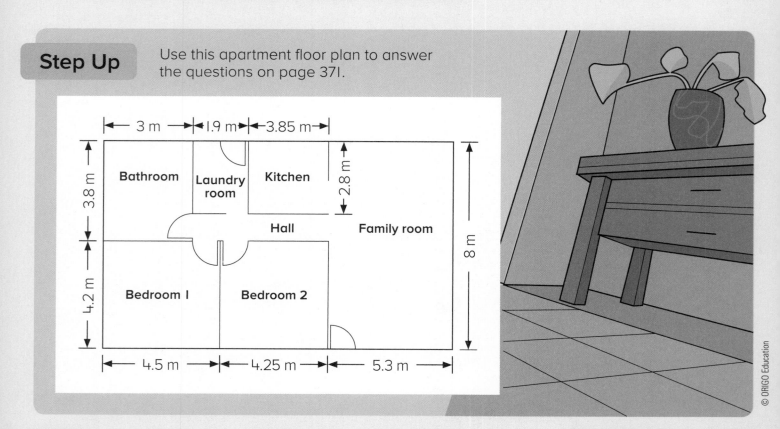

3 m, 1.9 m, 3.85 m

Bathroom, Laundry room, Kitchen

3.8 m, 2.8 m

Hall, Family room

8 m

4.2 m

Bedroom 1, Bedroom 2

4.5 m, 4.25 m, 5.3 m

Estimate, then calculate the area of each room on the plan on page 370.

a. Bedroom 1	b. Family room	c. Bathroom
Estimate _____ m²	Estimate _____ m²	Estimate _____ m²
_____ m²	_____ m²	_____ m²

d. Bedroom 2	e. Laundry room
Estimate _____ m²	Estimate _____ m²
_____ m²	_____ m²

Step Ahead

Calculate the area of the whole apartment on page 370. Show your thinking.

_____ m²

Step In

What steps would you follow to solve this problem?

There are 2 loaves of banana bread cut into tenths. Four-tenths are put into each plastic bag to be stored in the freezer.

How many plastic bags are stored in the freezer?

What division equation represents this problem?

$$\boxed{} \div \boxed{} = ?$$

Kyle drew this picture to help calculate the answer. Each square represents one whole.

How might it help to solve the problem?

How many times can you shade four-tenths so both squares are completely covered?

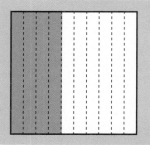
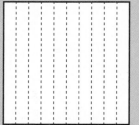

Complete the equation.

$$\boxed{} \div \boxed{} = \boxed{}$$

How would you calculate the quotient of 3 ÷ 0.2?

José and Carol thought about strategies they had used for dividing with common fractions.

José thought about it this way.

$? \times 0.2 = 3$

$? \times 2 \text{ tenths} = 30 \text{ tenths}$

Carol thought about it like this.

$? \times \dfrac{2}{10} = 3$

$? \times \dfrac{2}{10} = \dfrac{30}{10}$

What are they each doing to calculate the quotient?

Step Up

1. Each large square represents one whole. Complete each equation.

a.

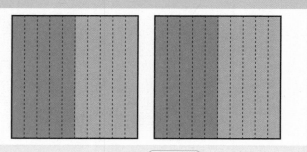

$2 \div 0.5 = \boxed{}$

b.

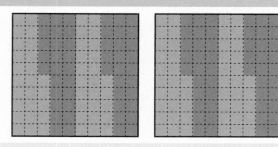

$2 \div 0.25 = \boxed{}$

2. Each large square represents one whole. Shade parts to match the equation, then write the quotient.

a.

$3 \div 0.1 =$ _____

b.

$2 \div 0.05 =$ _____

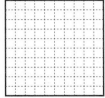

3. Complete each equation. Show your thinking.

a.

$7 \div 0.2 =$ _____

b.

$4 \div 0.01 =$ _____

4. Use multiplication to check the answers to the division problems.

a. $5 \div 0.2 = 10$

◯ Correct   ◯ Incorrect

b. $4 \div 0.5 = 8$

◯ Correct   ◯ Incorrect

c. $6 \div 0.1 = 6$

◯ Correct   ◯ Incorrect

d. $3 \div 0.25 = 12$

◯ Correct   ◯ Incorrect

Step Ahead

Terek knows that $1 \div 0.02 = 50$. How could he use this equation to calculate $4 \div 0.02$? Explain your thinking in words.

_____

_____

_____

Computation Practice

What do storms, needles, and potatoes have in common?

★ Complete the equations. Then write each letter above its matching product at the bottom of the page.

$12 \times 38 =$ ____ **y** $24 \times 12 =$ ____ **l** $18 \times 11 =$ ____ **u**

$31 \times 13 =$ ____ **n** $12 \times 42 =$ ____ **e** $13 \times 41 =$ ____ **a**

$21 \times 11 =$ ____ **h** $26 \times 12 =$ ____ **e** $33 \times 11 =$ ____ **s**

$11 \times 42 =$ ____ **t** $14 \times 18 =$ ____ **s** $12 \times 32 =$ ____ **h**

$13 \times 15 =$ ____ **t** $45 \times 11 =$ ____ **o** $22 \times 14 =$ ____ **a**

$43 \times 12 =$ ____ **b** $26 \times 11 =$ ____ **a** $13 \times 23 =$ ____ **e**

$14 \times 25 =$ ____ **e** $12 \times 18 =$ ____ **v** $11 \times 41 =$ ____ **e**

$34 \times 12 =$ ____ **n** $13 \times 35 =$ ____ **l** $45 \times 14 =$ ____ **t**

$11 \times 17 =$ ____ **y** $12 \times 25 =$ ____ **c** $14 \times 34 =$ ____ **e**

195	231	350	456	286	455	288	384	533	216	312

451	187	504	252	516	198	462

300	308	408	403	495	630	363	299	476

Ongoing Practice

1. Write the missing numbers to show equivalent capacity in each row. The first row has been done for you.

Milliliters	Liters (common fraction)	Liters (decimal fraction)
1,200	$1\frac{2}{10}$	1.2
	$2\frac{7}{10}$	
		0.8
5,100		
	$3\frac{6}{10}$	

2. Each large square represents one whole. Write the products. Shade parts of the squares to match.

a. $0.5 \times 0.3 =$ _____

b. $0.8 \times 0.4 =$ _____

c. $0.6 \times 0.8 =$ _____

Preparing for Module 11

Double one number and halve the other. Then write the products.

a. $12 \times 5 =$ _____

is the same value as

_____ × _____ = _____

b. $8 \times 15 =$ _____

is the same value as

_____ × _____ = _____

c. $6 \times 35 =$ _____

is the same value as

_____ × _____ = _____

d. $45 \times 6 =$ _____

is the same value as

_____ × _____ = _____

e. $35 \times 4 =$ _____

is the same value as

_____ × _____ = _____

f. $18 \times 15 =$ _____

is the same value as

_____ × _____ = _____

Step In

This pitcher holds 0.8 quarts of juice.
Four people share the juice equally.

How much juice does each person have?

What operation will you use to calculate the answer?

What equation would you write to show the problem?

It helps me remember that 0.8 is a fraction.

0.8 shared by 4 is equivalent to 8 tenths shared by 4.

This is like an unknown factor problem.

4 × ? = 0.8

Five flags are positioned at equal distances around the inside of an athletics track. The track's total length is 0.25 miles.

If you walk around the inside of the track, how far is it between each pair of flags?

25 hundredths divided by 5 is 5 hundredths. That's 0.05. It's important to record the answer as a decimal fraction.

Step Up

1. Complete the multiplication equation you would use to solve each division problem. Then write the quotient.

a.
0.12 ÷ 4 =

4 × _____ = 0.12

b.
0.45 ÷ 9 =

9 × _____ = 0.45

c.
0.36 ÷ 6 =

6 × _____ = 0.36

d.
0.90 ÷ 10 =

10 × _____ = 0.90

e.
0.07 ÷ 1 =

1 × _____ = 0.07

f.
0.60 ÷ 15 =

15 × _____ = 0.60

2. Complete each equation. Remember to write the quotient as a decimal fraction.
   Show your thinking, and check your answer by multiplying.

a.
$0.9 \div 3 = $ _____

b.
$0.8 \div 4 = $ _____

c.
$0.36 \div 9 = $ _____

d.
$0.06 \div 3 = $ _____

e.
$0.80 \div 20 = $ _____

f.
$0.01 \div 1 = $ _____

3. Solve each problem. Show your thinking.

a. Emma uses 0.6 kg of dog food to feed her 3 dogs. How much food will she give each dog?

_____ kg

b. A piece of lumber is marked into 9 equal lengths. Three lengths are cut off. The leftover piece is 0.48 meters long. How long is each marked piece?

_____ m

Step Ahead

Write a word problem to match the equation. Then complete the equation.

$0.72 \div 8 = $ _____

_____

_____

_____

_____

Step In

The blue ribbon below is 0.6 meters long. If the ribbon is cut into pieces that are each 0.2 meters long, how many pieces will there be?

0.6

0.9

I would use multiplication to calculate the number of pieces. That's _____ × 0.2 = 0.6.

The red ribbon is 0.9 meters long. If it is cut into 0.15 meter lengths, how many pieces will there be?

How could you use multiplication to calculate the answer?

What equation could you write?

Hmm ... 0.9 m is equivalent to 0.90 m. How could that help me?

Write a multiplication equation to solve each division problem.

Then write the quotient.

0.12 ÷ 0.03 = [   ]

0.42 ÷ 0.06 = [   ]

0.9 ÷ 0.1 = [   ]

Step Up

1. Complete the multiplication equation to solve each division problem. Then write the quotient.

a.
0.8 ÷ 0.2 = [   ]

[   ] × 0.2 = 0.8

b.
0.24 ÷ 0.06 = [   ]

[   ] × 0.06 = 0.24

c.
0.72 ÷ 0.08 = [   ]

[   ] × 0.08 = 0.72

d.
0.60 ÷ 0.15 = [   ]

[   ] × 0.15 = 0.60

e.
0.9 ÷ 0.3 = [   ]

[   ] × 0.3 = 0.9

f.
0.80 ÷ 0.20 = [   ]

[   ] × 0.20 = 0.80

2. Complete each equation. Show your thinking.

a.
$0.8 \div 0.4 = \underline{\quad}$

b.
$0.18 \div 0.03 = \underline{\quad}$

c.
$0.40 \div 0.04 = \underline{\quad}$

d.
$0.81 \div 0.09 = \underline{\quad}$

e.
$0.90 \div 0.30 = \underline{\quad}$

f.
$0.5 \div 0.1 = \underline{\quad}$

g.
$0.4 \div 0.08 = \underline{\quad}$

h.
$0.75 \div 0.01 = \underline{\quad}$

i.
$0.6 \div 0.12 = \underline{\quad}$

3. Solve each problem. Show your thinking.

a. A small pitcher holds 0.75 L of water. All the water is poured equally into some cups. There is 0.25 L of water in each cup. How many cups are there?

$\underline{\quad}$ cups

b. A block of cheese weighs 0.6 kg. The block is cut into smaller pieces. Each piece weighs 0.05 kg. How many pieces are there?

$\underline{\quad}$ pieces

Step Ahead

Rewrite the equation to show the correct quotient. Then write in words the mistake that was made.

$0.30 \div 0.1 = 30$

Think and Solve Same shapes have the same mass.

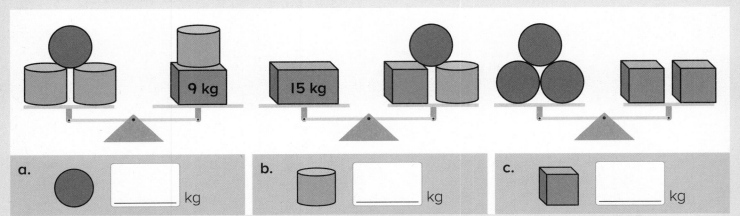

a. ⬤ _____ kg

b. ⬭ _____ kg

c. ⬛ _____ kg

Words at Work

Write in words how you solve this problem.

A large room has an area of 45 m². The length is 9 meters. A builder has to create a new wall to split the whole room as shown into two smaller rooms that are the same size. The wall will be 12 cm thick. What will be the area of each room?

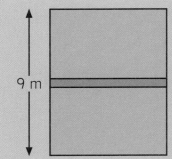

9 m

Ongoing Practice

1. Solve each problem. Show your thinking.

a. Three liters of juice and eight 375 mL cans of lemonade are poured into a large bowl to make punch. How much punch is in the bowl?

_____ mL

b. Karen blends $\frac{1}{5}$ liter of carrot juice and 250 mL of apple juice with 100 mL of cold water. She pours the mixture into 2 glasses that each hold 250 mL. How much of the mixture is left over?

_____ mL

2. Calculate the area of each room. Show your thinking.

a. Family room   6.7 m by 5.5 m

_____ m²

b. Laundry room   2.4 m by 2.1 m

_____ m²

Preparing for Module 11

Round one number and adjust the other to make it easier to add. Then complete the equation.

a. 46 + 98

is the same value as

____ + ____ = ____

b. 149 + 77

is the same value as

____ + ____ = ____

c. 53 + 137

is the same value as

____ + ____ = ____

d. 279 + 43

is the same value as

____ + ____ = ____

Step In   Circle the expression with the greatest quotient.

$$24 \div 6 = 4$$
Dividend   Divisor   Quotient

A $0.63 \div 9$ **B** $4 \div 0.5$ **C** $0.42 \div 0.02$ **D** $2 \div 0.05$

How did you decide which expression to circle?

Which expression has the quotient that is the least?

How can you tell without calculating each quotient?

The quotient for examples B, C, and D are all whole numbers. The quotient for example A is a decimal fraction.

What number would you write to complete this equation?

How did you decide? $\boxed{} \div 0.2 = 4$

I could use multiplication to figure out the missing dividend.

Step Up   1. Write a multiplication equation to solve each division problem. Then write the quotient.

a. $4 \div 0.1 =$ _____

b. $0.21 \div 0.03 =$ _____

c. $0.8 \div 0.4 =$ _____

d. $0.64 \div 8 =$ _____

e. $3 \div 0.02 =$ _____

f. $0.15 \div 0.03 =$ _____

g. $2 \div 0.04 =$ _____

h. $0.17 \div 1 =$ _____

i. $9 \div 0.5 =$ _____

2. Write the missing number to complete each equation. Show your thinking.

a. [   ] ÷ 0.1 = 2

b. 0.40 ÷ [   ] = 8

c. 0.8 ÷ [   ] = 4

d. 0.27 ÷ [   ] = 0.03

e. 3 ÷ [   ] = 6

f. [   ] ÷ 0.01 = 100

g. 0.56 ÷ [   ] = 0.07

h. [   ] ÷ 6 = 0.02

i. 2 ÷ [   ] = 8

3. Solve each problem. Show your thinking.

a. A walking track is 0.8 miles long. Ramon walks 4 miles in total. How many times did he walk the track?

[   ]

b. Koda buys 0.75 kg of carrots, which is 5 times the mass of the onion he also buys. How much does the onion weigh?

 [   ] kg

4. Write an equation to match each sentence. Use a letter for the unknown amount.

a. Divide 5 by 0.25, then multiply by 0.3

b. Subtract 0.8 from 6, then divide by 0.4

Step Ahead Write three different division equations that use at least one decimal fraction and have 6 as the quotient.

[   ] ÷ [   ] = 6   [   ] ÷ [   ] = 6   [   ] ÷ [   ] = 6

Step In

Julia knows that 2 ÷ 1 = 2.

She writes the quotient on this place-value slider.

H	T	O .	t	h
		2 .		

How could she adjust the slider to calculate 2 ÷ 0.1?

Write numbers on this place-value slider to show the quotient.

H	T	O .	t	h
		.		

How could she adjust the slider to calculate 2 ÷ 0.01?

Write numbers on this place-value slider to show the quotient.

H	T	O .	t	h
		.		

How would the slider move if you showed the quotient of 2 ÷ 10?

How does the size of the divisor affect how the digits move?

How could you use what you know to calculate 2 ÷ 0.001?

What about 2 ÷ 100?

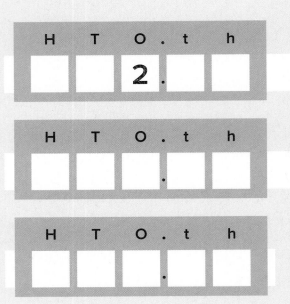

$$24 \div 6 = 4$$
Dividend   Divisor   Quotient

Step Up

1. Use a pattern to help you write the quotients in the place-value charts below.

a.

	Th	H	T	O .	t	h
60 ÷ 10 =						
60 ÷ 1 =						
60 ÷ 0.1 =						
60 ÷ 0.01 =						

b.

	Th	H	T	O .	t	h
40 ÷ 10 =						
40 ÷ 1 =						
40 ÷ 0.1 =						
40 ÷ 0.01 =						

2. Write the quotients in the place-value charts.

a.

	Th	H	T	O .	t	h
90 ÷ 30 =						
90 ÷ 3 =						
90 ÷ 0.3 =						
90 ÷ 0.03 =						

b.

	Th	H	T	O .	t	h
80 ÷ 20 =						
80 ÷ 2 =						
80 ÷ 0.2 =						
80 ÷ 0.02 =						

3. Look at each division chart. What happens when the divisor decreases by a factor of 10?

_____

_____

_____

4. Write in words how you could use this division fact to calculate 8 ÷ 0.04.

$8 \div 4 = 2$

_____

_____

_____

Step Ahead

Color **blue** the expressions that equal 300.
Color **red** the expressions that equal 30.

1,200 ÷ 4	120 ÷ 0.4	12 ÷ 0.4	120 ÷ 0.04
120 ÷ 4	1,200 ÷ 40	120 ÷ 40	12 ÷ 4

Working Space

Computation Practice — What does every winner lose in a triathlon?

★ Complete the equations. Then find each answer in the grid below and cross out the letter above. Write the remaining letters at the bottom of the page. Write the letters in order from the ✳ to the bottom-right corner.

1.62 + 9.3 = _____	8 – 1.67 = _____	3.7 + 2.42 = _____
2.31 – 1.64 = _____	1.7 + 2.96 = _____	3.45 – 0.7 = _____
2.58 + 0.9 = _____	1.24 – 0.38 = _____	6.9 + 1.37 = _____
2.96 – 0.7 = _____	1.53 + 7.2 = _____	7.7 – 2.99 = _____
5.91 + 1.2 = _____	3.02 – 1.5 = _____	0.82 + 1.88 = _____
1.62 – 0.09 = _____	3.08 + 1.07 = _____	1.09 – 0.49 = _____
4.73 + 1.91 = _____	4.73 – 1.91 = _____	2.04 + 1.07 = _____
2.04 – 1.07 = _____	2.8 + 2.17 = _____	4.9 – 1.05 = _____
2 – 0.95 = _____	1.24 + 0.77 = _____	3.22 + 3.92 = _____
3.75 + 2.35 = _____	3.04 – 0.8 = _____	

T	E	E	T	H	S	M	I	L	E	D	I	R	T
0.84	0.86	7.11	6.64	0.5	0.97	1.53	0.67	4.71	8.53	2.75	2.25	8.29	2.26

B	I	C	E	P	S	R	E	G	U	L	A	R
6.34	10.92	6.1	1.05	2.24	7.14	0.49	4.98	6.33	3.11	2.7	6.2	4.15

I	T	Y	S	H	I	R	T	S	H	I	P	S
4.97	3.48	0.6	8.73	2.01	3.85	6.12	5.11	4.66	7.13	8.27	1.52	2.82

Ongoing Practice

I. Draw a red needle to show the mass on the scale. Then write the mass two other ways.

a.
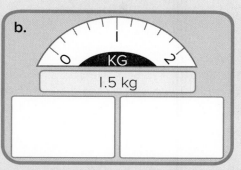
0.8 kg

b.
1.5 kg

c.
3,200 g

d.
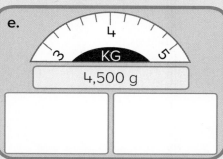
2 $\frac{1}{5}$ kg

e.
4,500 g

f.
2.75 kg

2. Each large square represents one whole. Shade or outline parts to help you figure out the quotients. Then complete the equations.

a.
2 ÷ 0.8 = _____

b.
2 ÷ 0.08 = _____

Preparing for Module II

Label the dimensions and write equations to calculate each partial product. Then add the partial products to calculate the total.

3 × 378

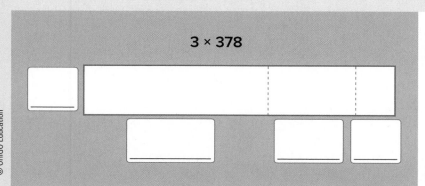

_____ × _____ = _____

_____ × _____ = _____

_____ × _____ = _____

Total _____

Step In

What strategy would you use to solve this division problem?

$4 \div 0.2 = \boxed{}$

I know there are 5 groups of 0.2 in one whole. So I need to figure out the number of groups in four wholes.

I must multiply 5 groups by 4, which is 20.

Samura uses a different strategy.

He multiplies the dividend and divisor by 10 to make an equivalent expression that is easier to calculate.

How does the diagram show his strategy?

Does the quotient remain the same? Why?

What happens if only one part of the equation is changed?

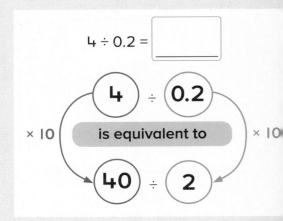

$4 \div 0.2 = \boxed{}$

$4 \div 0.2$

$\times 10$ is equivalent to $\times 10$

$40 \div 2$

How could you use the same strategy to calculate $6 \div 0.04$?

This time I'm working with hundredths, so I'll have to increase both the dividend and divisor by a factor of 100.

Step Up

1. Multiply the dividend and divisor by 10 or 100 to work with whole numbers. Then complete the equation.

a.

$3 \div 0.6 = \boxed{}$

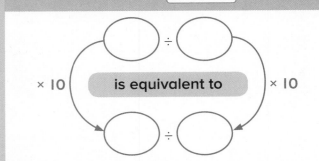

$\times 10$ is equivalent to $\times 10$

b.

$5 \div 0.01 = \boxed{}$

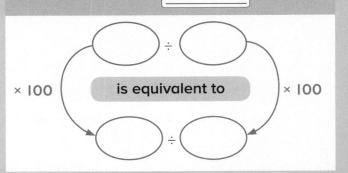

$\times 100$ is equivalent to $\times 100$

2. Complete each equation. You can use the diagram to help. Make sure you multiply both the dividend and divisor by the same factor.

a.

$8 \div 0.2 = \boxed{}$

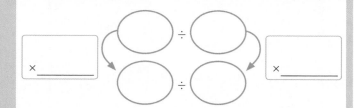

b.

$0.6 \div 0.3 = \boxed{}$

c.

$4 \div 0.05 = \boxed{}$

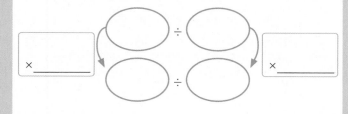

d.

$0.9 \div 0.3 = \boxed{}$

3. Use a strategy of your choice to complete these equations. Show your thinking.

a.

$6 \div 0.4 = \boxed{}$

b.

$0.08 \div 0.04 = \boxed{}$

c.

$3 \div 0.02 = \boxed{}$

Step Ahead

Complete these equations. Use different numbers and at least one decimal fraction in each equation.

a.

 $\times \boxed{} \div \boxed{} = 2$

b.

 $\times \boxed{} \div \boxed{} = 2$

Step In

Look at these equations. What do you know about the answers?

$4 \times 0.1 =$ _____ $4 \times 0.01 =$ _____ $4 \div 0.1 =$ _____ $4 \div 0.01 =$ _____

Which equations will have an answer that is greater than 4? Which will be less than 4?

Which equation will have the greatest answer? Which one will have the least?

How do you know?

How are these problems the same? How are they different?

Lilian is planning a camping trip. She will take 10 gallons of drinking water. If she uses about 0.5 gal of water each day, how long will the water last?

Chayton is planning a camping trip. He plans to be away for 10 days. If he uses about 0.5 gal of water each day, how much water will he need to take?

What steps would you use to calculate the answer to each problem?

What equation would you write to solve each problem?

Which answer will be greater? How do you know?

Step Up

1. In each pair, circle the expression that will have the **greater** answer. Show your thinking.

a.

8×0.5 **or** $8 \div 0.5$

b.

8×0.5 **or** 8×0.05

c.

8×0.05 **or** $8 \div 0.05$

d.

$8 \div 0.5$ **or** $8 \div 0.05$

2. Write an equation to represent each problem. Use a letter for the unknown amount. Then choose a method and show your thinking to calculate the answer.

a. Norton is cutting 9 pieces of fabric that are each 0.7 yd long. What is the total length of fabric he needs?

 yd

b. A water pipe loses 0.2 gallons of water every minute. How long will it take to lose 20 gallons of water?

 min

c. A newborn calf gains about 0.8 kg each day. How many days will it take to gain 24 kg?

 days

d. A large egg weighs about 0.06 kg. What will be the total mass of 8 large eggs?

 kg

3. Select the matching statement to describe the answer. You do not need to calculate the answer.

a. $6 \times (0.43 \div 15) = ?$

- ○ It will be one-sixth greater than $15 \div 0.43$.
- ○ It will be 6 times greater than $0.43 \div 15$.
- ○ It will be one-sixth of $15 \div 0.43$.
- ○ It will be one-sixth of $0.43 \div 15$.

b. $(5 + 0.13) \div 8 = ?$

- ○ It will be greater than 1 but less than 10.
- ○ It will be less than 1.
- ○ It will be greater than 10.
- ○ It will be between 1 and 10.

Step Ahead Complete this trail.

| 1.5 | → × 4 → | | → ÷ 0.6 → | |

| | ← − 0.1 ← | | ← ÷ 4 ← | | ← + 0.36 ← |

Think and Solve

a. Write a two-digit number and a three-digit number that belong in each part of this diagram.

b. Write a two-digit number and a three-digit number that do not belong in any part of the diagram.

Square numbers

A

B

Multiples of 2

C

D

E

F

G

Multiples of 3

Words at Work

Imagine your friend was away from school when you were learning how to adjust the dividend and the divisor to solve a problem such as 0.8 ÷ 0.04. Explain the thinking and the steps in words.

Ongoing Practice

1. Solve each problem. Show your thinking.

a. Yasmin needs 3.25 kg of ground beef to make sausages. She only has 900 g in the freezer. How much more does she need to buy?

_____ kg

b. Joel buys 1.78 kg of ground beef, 700 grams of chicken fillets, and $2\frac{3}{4}$ kg of beef ribs. How much meat does he buy in total?

_____ kg

FROM 5.9.11

2. Complete each equation. You can use the diagram to help.

a.
$4 \div 0.2 =$

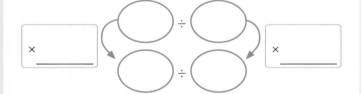

b.
$0.8 \div 0.4 =$

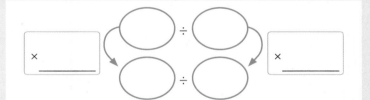

FROM 5.10.11

c.
$8 \div 0.5 =$

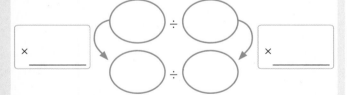

d.
$4 \div 0.04 =$

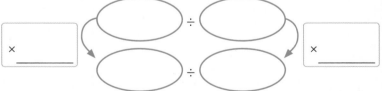

Preparing for Module 11

Solve each problem. Show your thinking. Remember to write the units in your answers.

a. The area of a gymnasium floor is 300 square yards. The shorter sides measure 12 yards. How long is the floor?

b. Two sides of a triangular playground measure 24 ft and 17 ft. The perimeter is 62 ft. How long is the remaining side?

Step In

Steven is drawing a border around the edge of a page, using shapes to make a pattern. A section of it is shown below.

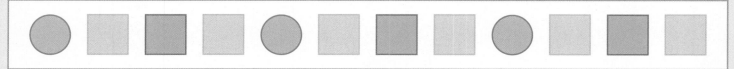

What part of the pattern repeats? What shape should come next?
If Steven drew 5 circles, how many squares should he draw? How do you know?
If he drew 42 more squares, how many circles should he draw?

Arleen has a number of seedlings to plant in rows.
This rule describes how many seedlings will be needed.

Number of rows × 8 = Number of seedlings

How many seedlings will be planted in 3 rows? In 10 rows?
How do you calculate the answers?

How many rows will be needed for 32 seedlings? For 100 seedlings?
How do you calculate the answers?

Complete this table to show the relationship between the number of rows and the number of seedlings.

Number of rows	1	2		
Number of seedlings			40	72

Step Up

1. Read the rules, then complete the tables.

a. Number of squares × 2 = Number of circles

Number of squares	1	2	5		40	100
Number of circles	2			30		

b. Number of tires ÷ 5 = Number of cars

Number of tires	5	10			35	100
Number of cars	1		5	9		

For Questions 2 and 3, read about each situation then write the answers. Use the table to help.

2. A factory puts 6 bolts in a single packet.

Number of packets	1					
Number of bolts	6					

a. Write the number of bolts in: 5 packets ⬚ _____ 41 packets ⬚ _____

b. How many packets are needed for 120 bolts? ⬚ _____

3. A shoe factory uses 9 mL of glue for every pair of children's shoes.

Number of shoes	2					
Amount of glue (mL)	9					

a. Write the amount of glue used for: 12 shoes ⬚ _____ mL 19 shoes ⬚ _____ mL

b. How many shoes can be made with 360 mL of glue? ⬚ _____ shoes

4. a. A packet of noodles is $1.50. Make a table to match the situation. Show the results for different quantities of noodles.

b. Use the relationship between the noodles and price to write a question for another student to answer.

_____

Step Ahead

Beth saves some pocket money each month. At the end of each month Beth's mom gives her the amount she has saved multiplied by itself. In May, Beth plans to save $3, so her mom will give her $9.

a. How much will Beth have in savings at the end of May if she follows her plan? $ _____

b. If Beth wants to have about $130 in savings at the end of May, how many dollars would she need to save? Show your thinking on page 432. $ _____

Algebra: Examining relationships between two numerical patterns

Step In

A cafeteria is making a pasta sauce.

A large pot of sauce includes six cans of tomatoes and three onions. How many cans of tomatoes will be used if there are nine onions?

Tables can be used to help calculate the correct amounts for any number of pots of sauce.

A table can be made for each ingredient.

Number of pots	1	2	3	4	5
Cans of tomatoes	6	12			

Number of pots	1	2	3	4	5
Number of onions	3	6			

A table can also be made to show each ingredient at the same time.

Number of pots	1	2	3	4	5
Cans of tomatoes	6	12			
Number of onions	3	6			

Step Up

1. Emilio has a favorite fruit punch recipe. To make one glass of punch he uses 2 fl oz of pineapple juice and 6 fl oz of orange juice. Write in this table to help you answer the questions below.

Number of glasses	1					
Pineapple juice (fl oz)	2					
Orange juice (fl oz)	6					

a. How much pineapple juice will be used for 5 glasses of punch? _____ fl oz

b. If 12 fl oz of orange juice is used, how many glasses of punch can be made? _____

c. How much orange juice will be used if 20 fl oz of pineapple juice is used? _____ fl oz

d. How much pineapple juice will be used if 90 fl oz of orange juice is used? _____ fl oz

2. A lion and her cub are in a zoo. The lion is fed 12 lb of meat each day, and her cub has half as much. Make a table to help you answer the questions below.

a. How much meat in total will the lion have eaten after 3 days? _____ lb

b. If the cub has eaten 36 lb of meat in total, how much has the lion eaten? _____ lb

c. Write a question for another student to answer.

_____
_____

3. Read the rule for each person and complete the table.

Zoe's total savings = Number of weeks × $9   Dara's total savings = Number of weeks × $3

Number of weeks	1				
Zoe's total savings ($)	9				
Dara's total savings ($)	3				

4. a. How many times greater are Zoe's savings than Dara's savings? _____

b. How do you know?

_____

Step Ahead   Look at this pattern.

How often will a circle be red?

_____

Computation Practice

★ These students were given a math quiz. Check their answers and draw a ✔ beside each correct answer. Add the ✔ for each student and write the score at the bottom of each paper.

Vincent

Name:

1. $(280 - 40) \div 6 =$ **40**
2. $60 \times 15 \div 3 =$ **30**
3. $32 \div 8 + 8 =$ **2**
4. $120 - 4 \times 21 =$ **36**
5. $3 \times 20 \div 5 =$ **12**
6. $7 + 150 \div 3 =$ **52**
7. $240 \div (23 + 17) =$ **6**
8. $64 - 32 \div 8 =$ **4**
9. $(25 + 11) \div 6 =$ **6**
10. $7 \times 7 - 7 =$ **42**
11. $8 \times 11 - 5 =$ **83**
12. $8 \times (11 - 5) =$ **48**
13. $180 \div 90 \times 9 =$ **18**
14. $48 \div 12 - 2 =$ **2**
15. $(50 - 2) \div 12 =$ **4**
16. $96 \div 3 \times 2 =$ **64**
17. $77 \div (7 + 4) =$ **7**
18. $77 \div 7 + 4 =$ **7**
19. $11 \times (11 - 9) =$ **22**
20. $3 \times 8 + 4 =$ **36**

Total correct: _____

Sharon

Name:

1. $(280 - 40) \div 6 =$ **40**
2. $60 \times 15 \div 3 =$ **30**
3. $32 \div 8 + 8 =$ **12**
4. $120 - 4 \times 21 =$ **1,392**
5. $3 \times 20 \div 5 =$ **12**
6. $7 + 150 \div 3 =$ **57**
7. $240 \div (23 + 17) =$ **6**
8. $64 - 32 \div 8 =$ **60**
9. $(25 + 11) \div 6 =$ **6**
10. $7 \times 7 - 7 =$ **42**
11. $8 \times 11 - 5 =$ **83**
12. $8 \times (11 - 5) =$ **48**
13. $180 \div 90 \times 9 =$ **18**
14. $48 \div 12 - 2 =$ **3**
15. $(50 - 2) \div 12 =$ **4**
16. $96 \div 3 \times 2 =$ **16**
17. $77 \div (7 + 4) =$ **7**
18. $77 \div 7 + 4 =$ **15**
19. $11 \times (11 - 9) =$ **22**
20. $3 \times 8 + 4 =$ **28**

Total correct: _____

Who won the quiz? _____

Ongoing Practice

1. Draw and color an array to match each equation.
Then write the product.

a.

$\dfrac{2}{5} \times \dfrac{2}{3} = \underline{}$

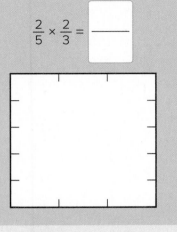

b.

$\dfrac{3}{4} \times \dfrac{1}{3} = \underline{}$

c.

$\dfrac{4}{6} \times \dfrac{1}{4} = \underline{}$

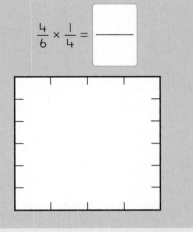

2. Read the rules then complete the tables.

a. Number of triangles ÷ 7 = Number of pentagons

Number of triangles	7	21	35			140
Number of pentagons	1			10	15	

b. Number of vases × 8 = Number of flowers

Number of vases	1		5	9		
Number of flowers	8	16			56	160

Preparing for Module 12

In each rectangle divide the parts then complete the equation.

a.

$75 \div 5 = \underline{}$

5 | 50 | 25

$\underline{} + \underline{}$

b.

$91 \div 7 = \underline{}$

7 | 70 | 21

$\underline{} + \underline{}$

Algebra: Introducing the coordinate plane

Step In

Imagine you took two number lines and turned one of them 90 degrees so that they intersect at 0.

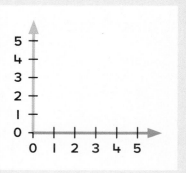

You can identify a point **on** the horizontal number line, or a point **on** the vertical number line.

You can also identify a point between the two number lines by making a grid.

On this grid, the horizontal number line is called the **x-axis**.
The vertical number line is called the **y-axis**.
The **origin** is where the two number lines intersect.

The position of the red point in the grid on the right can be described using **coordinates**, or an **ordered pair**.

The first number in an ordered pair is the **x-coordinate**.
It tells the distance to move from the origin along the x-axis.

The second number is the **y-coordinate**. It tells the distance to move from the origin along the y-axis.

The coordinates of the blue point in the grid are (2, 5).

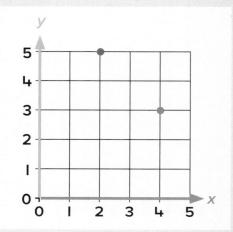

What are the coordinates of the red point? (☐ , ☐)

> The grid can be called a **coordinate grid** or **coordinate plane**.
> It is easy to remember which axis you work with first. Just think *crawl before you climb*.

Step Up

1. Mark and label each of these ordered pairs on the coordinate plane.

A (2, 3)   B (6, 1)   C (0, 2)

D (1, 4)   E (8, 4)   F (5, 0)

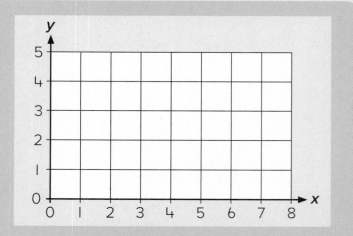

2. a. Write the ordered pair for each point marked on the coordinate plane below.

A (_____ , _____)   B (_____ , _____)   C (_____ , _____)

D (_____ , _____)   E (_____ , _____)   F (_____ , _____)

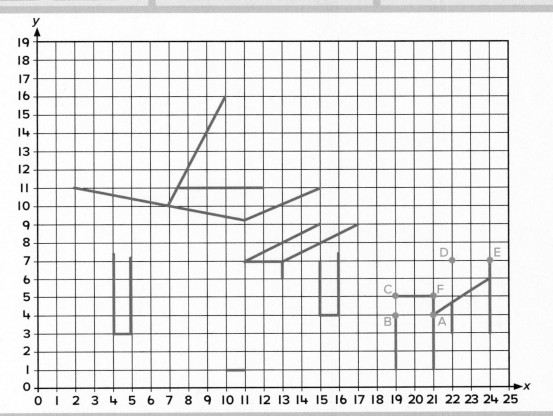

b. Mark and label each of these points on the coordinate plane above.

G (10, 1)	H (10, 6)	I (2, 8)	J (2, 11)	K (1, 13)	L (2, 15)
M (6, 16)	N (7, 18)	O (11, 18)	P (10, 16)	Q (12, 11)	R (15, 11)
S (15, 9)	T (17, 9)	U (17, 8)	V (13, 6)	W (11, 6)	X (11, 1)

c. Draw lines to connect points A to F in alphabetical order.

d. Draw lines to connect points G to X in alphabetical order.

Step Ahead

Two teams are trying to find each other's base in a game.
Each team has a map with a coordinate plane on it.
Team A has heard that Team B's base is at a certain position on the map.
When added together the coordinates for the base have a total of 7.
Write all the possible ordered pairs for Team B's base.

Step In

Sandra wrote the coordinates for the vertices of this shape.

Instead of listing the numbers in parentheses, she arranged them in a table.

	x-coordinate	y-coordinate
A	1	4
B	4	3
C	7	4
D	4	1

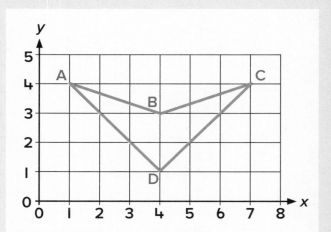

Complete this table to match the shape on the right. What do you notice about the headings of the table?

	y-coordinate	x-coordinate
E	4	3
F		
G		
H		

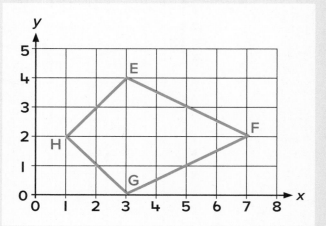

Ordered pairs always have the x-coordinate first. Tables may have **either** the x-coordinate or y-coordinate first.

Write the matching ordered pairs for E, F, G, and H.

(____ , ____) (____ , ____) (____ , ____) (____ , ____)

Step Up

1. Look at the table below. Mark the coordinates on the coordinate plane.

x-coordinate	y-coordinate
1	2
3	4
6	1
3	1
3	2

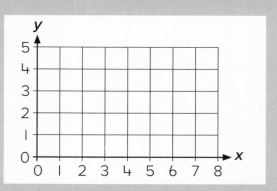

2. Rewrite each table or list of ordered pairs. Be sure to check the headings of each table before writing your answers.

a.

x-coordinate	2	5	8	10
y-coordinate	6	15	24	30

(_____ , _____) (_____ , _____)

(_____ , _____) (_____ , _____)

b.

x	y

(1, 3.4)   (4, 6.4)   (8.1, 10.5)   (6.6, 9)

c.

y	x
1	2
4	5
0	1
7	8

(_____ , _____)

(_____ , _____)

(_____ , _____)

(_____ , _____)

d.   (1, 5)   (3, 15)   (6, 30)   (2, 10)

x-coordinate			
y-coordinate			

e.

x	1	4	9	16
y	1	2	3	4

(_____ , _____) (_____ , _____)

(_____ , _____) (_____ , _____)

f.   (26, 21)   (19, 14)   (22, 17)   (40, 35)

y-coordinate			
x-coordinate			

Step Ahead

a. Mark the ordered pairs from Question 2c on this coordinate plane.

b. Draw a straight line to connect the points.

c. Write three other ordered pairs that are also on the line.

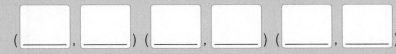

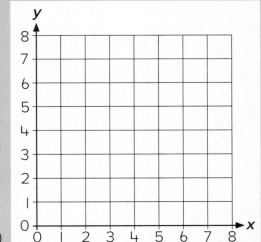

Think and Solve

What is the mystery number? ——

It is an improper fraction.

It is greater than 2.

It is less than 3.

Its numerator is 5 less than 3 times its denominator.

The sum of the digits of its denominator is 2.

Working Space

Words at Work

Write the answer for each clue in the grid. Use words from the list. Some words are not used.

Clues Across
4. The position of a point on a grid can be described using ___ pairs.
6. A coordinate grid can also be called a coordinate ___.
7. In an ordered pair, the ___ number is the y-coordinate.

Clues Down
1. In a coordinate grid, the ___ is where the x-axis and y-axis intersect.
2. To remember which axis to work with first, think ___ before you climb.
3. The x-coordinate is always written first in ordered ___.
5. When there is more than one axis, they are called ___.

Word list:
- coordinate
- second
- first
- pairs
- ordered
- crawl
- plane
- plain
- axes
- points
- numbers
- origin
- start
- apex

© ORIGO Education

Ongoing Practice

I. Calculate each product in two ways.

a.

$5 \times 3\frac{1}{3}$

Multiply the parts	Use improper fractions

b.

$4 \times 6\frac{1}{2}$

Multiply the parts	Use improper fractions

2. Write each set of coordinates as a list of ordered pairs.

a.

x-coordinate	0	2	4	6
y-coordinate	7.3	8.5	5.6	6.9

(_____ , _____) (_____ , _____)

(_____ , _____) (_____ , _____)

b.

y-coordinate	1	3	5	9
x-coordinate	4.0	6.2	7.1	8.6

(_____ , _____) (_____ , _____)

(_____ , _____) (_____ , _____)

Preparing for Module 12

Partition each dividend into parts that are easier to divide. Then complete the equations. Show your thinking.

a.
$348 \div 4 =$ [____]

b.
$435 \div 3 =$ [____]

c.
$762 \div 6 =$ [____]

Step In

A school is having a bake sale. For every $2 that is spent on ingredients the school earns $6 in sales. If $8 is spent on ingredients, how much should the school expect to earn?

Complete this table to help your thinking.

Amount spent ($)	2	10	8
Amount earned ($)			

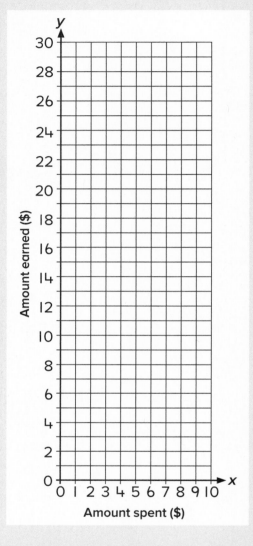

The data from the table can also be shown on a coordinate plane.

Write each pair of values from the table as ordered pairs, with the amount spent in dollars as the *x*-coordinate.

(_____ , _____) (_____ , _____) (_____ , _____)

Mark the coordinates on the coordinate plane.

How could you use the graph to calculate how much the school would earn if $6 was spent?

At the next bake sale, $8 is earned for every $3 spent on ingredients.

How can you use the graph to figure out whether this is better or worse than the previous bake sale?

Step Up

1. a. Olivia is going to the state fair, which runs for a week. For $12 she can buy 4 tickets for the rides. Complete the table to show the different number of tickets she can buy.

Amount spent (x)	$12	$48	$96	$24	$72
Number of tickets (y)					

b. Write each pair of values as an ordered pair.

(_____ , _____) (_____ , _____) (_____ , _____) (_____ , _____) (_____ , _____)

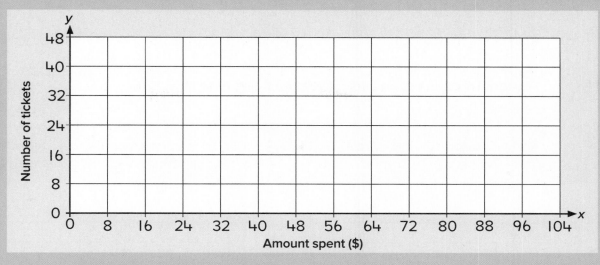

2. Mark the coordinates from Question 1 on the grid above. Then draw a line to connect them all.

3. Olivia's cousin Michael lives in a different state. For $16 he can buy 8 tickets for rides.

Complete the table, then write each pair of values as an ordered pair.

Amount spent (x)	$16	$80	$96	$32
Number of tickets (y)				

(_____ , _____) (_____ , _____)

(_____ , _____) (_____ , _____)

4. Mark the coordinates from Question 3 on the grid above. Then draw a line to connect them all.

5. Use the coordinate grid to answer the questions below.

a. Imagine Olivia and a friend share the cost of some tickets.
If Olivia wants 20 tickets, how much money should she contribute? $ _____

b. Imagine Michael and a friend share the cost of some tickets.
If Michael contributes $24, how many tickets should he get? _____ tickets

---

Step Ahead

Alexis and Felix each get pocket money on a Friday. On Monday of Week 1, Alexis already has $10 and plans to save $4 each Friday. Felix has no money, but plans to save $6 each Friday. At the start of which week will Felix have more in total savings than Alexis?

Make a table to help explain your answer.

Week _____

Algebra: Interpreting coordinate grids

Step In   A scout troop is organizing a weekend camping trip.

The grid below shows the number of cars needed to transport the scouts to camp.

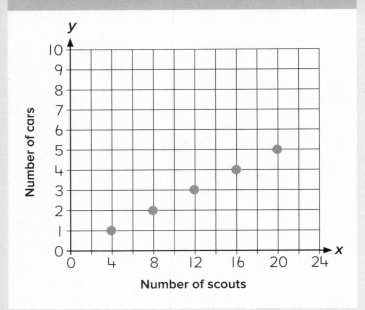

The grid below shows how many cups of water it is estimated each scout will drink each day.

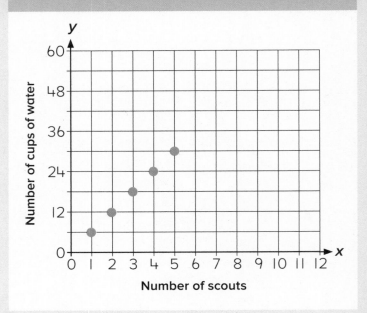

How many cups of water will 6 scouts drink? How do you know?
How many scouts can be catered for with 18 cups of water?

How many scouts can be transported by 5 cars?
How many cars will be needed to transport 17 scouts?

Does it make sense to draw a line to connect the points on each grid? Why?

Step Up

1. Look at the grid that shows the relationship between the number of cars and scouts. Record the ordered pair for each point that is shown on that grid.

2. Look at the grid that shows the relationship between the number of cups of water and scouts. Record the ordered pairs for each point that is shown on that grid.

3. A plane moves at a constant speed
in a straight line from a starting point.
The grid on the right shows the distance
from the start at points in time.

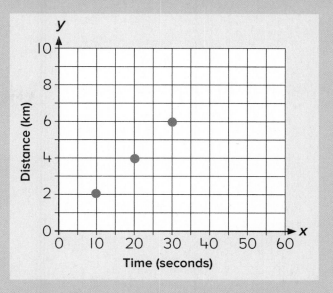

a. Record the ordered pair for each point shown.

b. Mark the point to show the distance
at 50 seconds.

c. How far will the plane have
traveled at 15 seconds?

d. How long will the plane have traveled
to reach 9 kilometers?

4. A necklace has a certain number of red
beads for a certain number of green beads.
The grid on the right shows the relationship
between the beads.

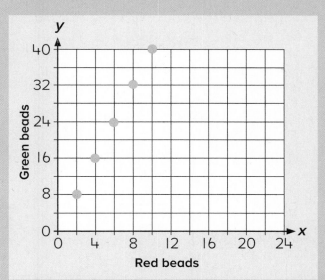

a. How many green beads would
be used with five red beads?

b. Record the ordered pairs for three points.

c. Record the ordered pairs in this table.

Red beads (x)			
Green beads (y)			

Step Ahead This rule describes the relationship between the number of cups of water (C)
and number of scouts (S) on page 410: **S × 6 = C**

Write rules to describe the relationship between the items in Questions 3 and 4.

a. Distance (D) and Time (T): _____

b. Green beads (G) and Red beads (R): _____

Computation Practice

Why do firefighters wear red suspenders?

★ Complete the equations. Then find each product in the puzzle below and color its matching letter.

$3.7 \times 4 =$ ___

$5.7 \times 3 =$ ___

$2 \times 4.8 =$ ___

$5 \times 3.8 =$ ___

$6 \times 5.8 =$ ___

$5.6 \times 4 =$ ___

$6.4 \times 3 =$ ___

$2 \times 3.6 =$ ___

$5 \times 4.7 =$ ___

$7 \times 4.3 =$ ___

$6.3 \times 4 =$ ___

$7.8 \times 3 =$ ___

$5.3 \times 3 =$ ___

$8 \times 3.8 =$ ___

$4 \times 5.4 =$ ___

$3 \times 8.9 =$ ___

$6.7 \times 2 =$ ___

$2.7 \times 9 =$ ___

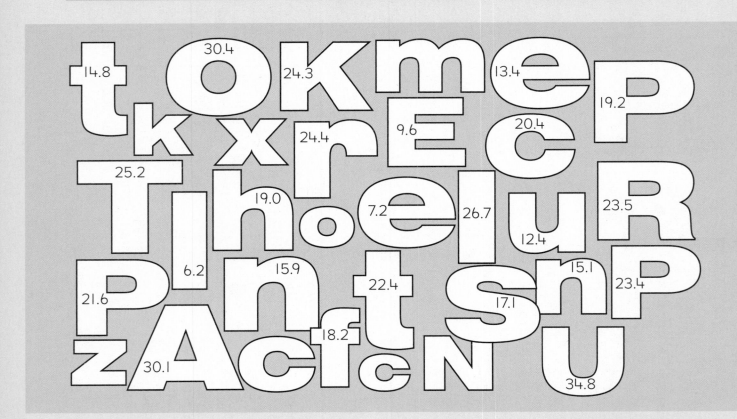

Ongoing Practice

1. Rewrite the equation by converting each mixed number to an improper fraction. Then write the product.

a.

$$\frac{2}{5} \times 1\frac{1}{3} =$$

b.

$$3\frac{1}{4} \times \frac{2}{3} =$$

c.

$$\frac{7}{4} \times 1\frac{1}{2} =$$

d.

$$\frac{5}{2} \times 1\frac{5}{6} =$$

e.

$$2\frac{1}{4} \times \frac{1}{5} =$$

f.

$$3\frac{1}{8} \times \frac{4}{3} =$$

FROM 5.8.10

2. Claire earns up to $8 doing different chores each week. Every week, she gives $1 of her money to charity and saves the rest.

a. Write four different weekly earnings amounts in the table below, then show how much Claire saved from each amount. Remember, all earnings must be $8 or less.

Earnings ($)				
Savings ($)				

b. Graph the coordinates from the table onto the coordinate grid.

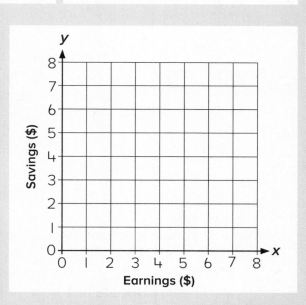

FROM 5.11.5

Preparing for Module 12

Use a partitioning strategy to divide. Show your thinking.

a.

$$314 \div 5 = \underline{\qquad}$$ remainder

b.

$$1568 \div 3 = \underline{\qquad}$$ remainder

SPACE ADVENTURE

$1.25

Issue 43

Step In

How could you calculate the cost of buying 12 issues of this comic book?

I double doubled $1.25 to figure out the cost of 4 issues. That's $5, and 12 × $1.25 is the same value as 3 × $5, which is $15.

I know that 10 issues cost $12.50 and 2 issues cost $2.50. That's $15 in total.

Emilia used the double-and-halve strategy. Write how you think she figured out the cost.

Use Emilia's strategy to calculate this product.

12 × $1.50 = $_____

is the same value as

_____ × _____ = _____

How did you decide which factor to double and which factor to halve?

Step Up

1. **Double** one number and **halve** the other to make a problem that is easier to solve. If necessary, repeat this step then write the product.

a.

4 × $1.75 = $_____

_____ × _____

_____ × _____

b.

6 × $2.50 = $_____

_____ × _____

_____ × _____

c.

4 × $1.25 = $_____

_____ × _____

_____ × _____

2. Double and halve to solve these.

a.
6 × $0.75 = $_____

_____ × _____

_____ × _____

b.
$1.25 × 16 = $_____

_____ × _____

_____ × _____

c.
24 × $0.75 = $_____

_____ × _____

_____ × _____

d.
$0.25 × 16 = $_____

_____ × _____

_____ × _____

e.
32 × $1.50 = $_____

_____ × _____

_____ × _____

f.
8 × $1.75 = $_____

_____ × _____

_____ × _____

3. Use the same strategy to calculate these.

a.
4 × $3.50 = $_____

b.
8 × $1.25 = $_____

c.
8 × $2.50 = $_____

d.
16 × $0.50 = $_____

e.
16 × $0.75 = $_____

f.
24 × $0.25 = $_____

4. Write some equations involving money that you can solve by doubling and halving.

a.
_____ × _____ = _____

b.
_____ × _____ = _____

c.
_____ × _____ = _____

d.
_____ × _____ = _____

Step Ahead

Hassun has $20 to spend on comic books.
Write the greatest number of each issue he can buy.

ACTION COMICS $1.75

_____ issues

DETECTIVE MYSTERY $1.45

_____ issues

SPOOKY STORIES $2.25

_____ issues

Step In

How would you calculate the total cost of two cans of mango juice?

MANGO JUICE

$3.49

I doubled $3.50 and adjusted my answer back 2 cents.

Write an equation to show your strategy.

Use the same strategy to calculate the total cost of three cans of tuna.

Write an equation to show your thinking.

$2.98   TUNA

Imagine you used the same strategy to calculate the cost of four loaves of bread.

Write a dollar-and-cent amount on the price tag.
Then write an equation to show how you would calculate the total cost.

BREAD

Step Up

I. Calculate the total cost. Try rounding, then adjusting your answer.

a.
Buy 3. $2.98

$ _____

b.
Buy 2. $5.98

$ _____

c.
Buy 4. Cereal $3.99

$ _____

2. Write the total cost.

a. Buy 2 at $6.99 each.

$_____

b. Buy 3 at $6.97 each.

$_____

c. Buy 3 at $8.99 each.

$_____

d. Buy 4 at $3.49 each.

$_____

e. Buy 5 at $4.49 each.

$_____

f. Buy 6 at $5.48 each.

$_____

3. Shade the ⬭ beside each correct product.

a. $4.98 × 5 = $24.90 ⬭   **b.** $3.99 × 4 = $15.94 ⬭   **c.** $6.98 × 3 = $20.94 ⬭

d. $5.49 × 3 = $16.47 ⬭   **e.** $2.48 × 4 = $9.92 ⬭   **f.** $4.49 × 4 = $17.94 ⬭

4. Rewrite the incorrect equations from Question 3 with the product.

_____

_____

Step Ahead   Round and adjust each of these prices to calculate the total cost.

Music Downloads – $0.99 each song	
Songs	Cost ($)
1	0.99
2	
3	
5	
10	

Movie Downloads – $3.98 each movie	
Movies	Cost ($)
1	3.98
2	
3	
5	
10	

Think and Solve The ▱ means **multiply the two numbers together then subtract the sum of both numbers.**   5 ▱ 4 = 11

Look at these and figure out what ⭐ is doing.

Complete these.

5 ⭐ 2 = 27   10 ⭐ 0 = 100
3 ⭐ 1 = 10   6 ⭐ 4 = 40

a.
2 ⭐ [____] = 19

b.
[____] ⭐ 11 = 20

c.
7 ⭐ [____] = 53

d.
[____] ⭐ 1 = 65

e. What is ⭐ doing?

[_____]

Words at Work   Write in words how you would solve this problem.

One market stall is including a free pumpkin worth $3 with every purchase over $10.
Another market stall is including a bag of corn cobs worth $2.50 for every $10 spent.
A third market stall is giving $5 cash back for every $25 spent.
Which market stall is giving the best value for money for a purchase of $100?

Ongoing Practice

1. Color the ◯ to show whether the problem is multiplication or division. Then calculate the answer. Show your thinking.

a. Two people equally share $\frac{1}{4}$ gallon of water. How much water will be in each share?

◯ Multiplication ◯ Division

◻ ―――― gallon

b. Four hamsters weigh $\frac{1}{3}$ of a pound in total. If they are all about the same size, how much does each hamster weigh?

◯ Multiplication ◯ Division

◻ ―――― pound

2. Calculate the total cost. Try rounding, then adjusting your answer.

a. Buy 4 at $3.98 each.

$_____

b. Buy 3 at $5.99 each.

$_____

c. Buy 4 at $3.49 each.

$_____

Preparing for Module 12

Use factors or a partitioning strategy to divide. Show your thinking.

a.
$780 \div 30 =$ ◻

b.
$1{,}640 \div 40 =$ ◻

Step In

What is the total cost of four bottles of juice? How do you know?

Amos used a doubling strategy to figure it out. Show what you think he did.	Dallas multiplied the dollars and cents separately. Show what you think she did.

Is there another way you could calculate the total cost?

Use one of these strategies to calculate the cost of buying four tubs of ice cream.

Step Up

1. Use the prices above. Calculate the cost of buying **three** of these. Try multiplying the whole dollars and then the cents. Record the steps you use.

a. Oats	b. Shampoo	c. Flour
$_____	$_____	$_____

2. Use the prices above. Calculate the cost of buying **six** of these. Show your thinking.

a. Ice cream	b. Juice	c. Butter
$_____	$_____	$_____

Use the prices on page 420 to answer Questions 3, 4, and 5.

3. Calculate the cost of buying **five** of these. Show your thinking.

a. Ice cream

$ _____

b. Shampoo

$ _____

c. Flour

$ _____

4. Calculate the cost of buying **eight** of these. Show your thinking.

a. Butter

$ _____

b. Ice cream

$ _____

c. Juice

$ _____

5. Imagine you wanted to buy four of each item in Question 4.
Write how you could use your answers above to calculate each total.

_____

Step Ahead Write the missing numbers.

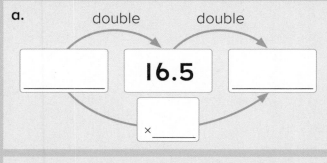

a. double   double

[_____] **16.5** [_____]

× _____

b. double   double

[_____] **4.7** [_____]

× _____

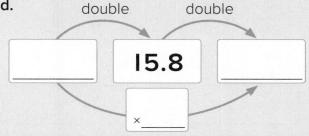

c. double   double

[_____] **13** [_____]

× _____

d. double   double

[_____] **15.8** [_____]

× _____

© ORIGO Education

Step In

The parks department is laying edging around the outside of a playground. The playground is rectangular, and the length is four times the width. The width measures 7.4 m.

How can you calculate the perimeter of the playground?

Isaac figured it out like this.

$$W = 7.4 \text{ m} \qquad P = (2 \times L) + (2 \times W)$$
$$L = 4 \times 7.4 \qquad P = (2 \times 29.6) + (2 \times 7.4)$$
$$L = 29.6 \text{ m} \qquad P = 59.2 + 14.8$$
$$P = 74 \text{ m}$$

You could also add the length and width first, then multiply the total by 2.

The edging for the playground is sold in strips that are 50 cm long. How many strips will be needed for the playground project?

1 m = 100 cm
1 m = 1,000 mm
1 cm = 10 mm

What steps will you follow to figure out the solution?

I know that 50 cm is equal to $\frac{1}{2}$ a meter. I need edging strips for at least 74 meters.

Step Up

1. Use the centimeter ruler to calculate the perimeter of the square. Show your thinking.

0 cm 1 2 3 4 5 6 7

Perimeter _____

2. Solve each problem. Show your thinking. Remember to write the unit of measurement.

a. Luis's sheet of paper is 10 cm wide and 12 cm long. The perimeter of Kay's sheet of paper is 176 cm. How many times longer is the perimeter of Kay's paper than Luis's?

b. The perimeter of a kite is 3.2 m. The 2 short sides are equal and the 2 long sides are equal. One long side measures 91 cm. What is the length of one short side?

c. A community playground is being fenced. It has 8 sides and a perimeter of 45 m. Four sides are each 375 cm long. All the other sides are equal. What is the length of one of the unknown sides?

d. Tyler is making 6 identical rectangular picture frames. Each frame is 24 cm long, which is twice the width. He has 5 meters of lumber. How much will he have left over after making the frames?

Step Ahead   Solve this problem. Show your thinking on page 432.

Ribbon is to be sewn around the edge of a school banner that is 3 meters long by 1.25 meters wide. The ribbon is sold in whole meters only and is $6.27 a meter. What is the total cost of the ribbon required?

$ _____

Computation Practice

What kind of coat can you put on only when it is wet?

★ Use a ruler to draw a straight line to the matching product. The line will pass through a number and a letter. Write each letter above its matching number at the bottom of the page.

Products

$1.40 × 3	$8.70
5 × $1.80	$4.20
3 × $2.50	$9.50
$2.40 × 4	$4.80
$2.90 × 3	$9.00
5 × $1.90	$7.80
$1.80 × 4	$9.30
3 × $1.60	$7.60
$3.10 × 3	$7.50
5 × $1.40	$7.00
$1.90 × 4	$7.20
3 × $2.60	$9.60

o   6   o   a   l   o   11   3   n   4   12   9   a   8   t   a   f   t   7   10   c   2   i   5   p

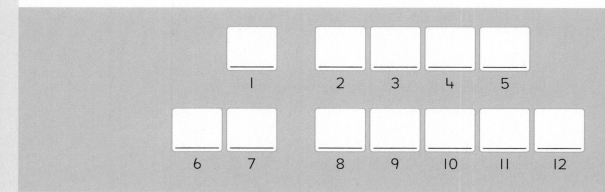

1	2	3	4	5

6	7	8	9	10	11	12

Ongoing Practice

I. Complete each equation. Show your thinking.

a.

$6 \times (\frac{1}{8} \div 5) = \boxed{}$

b.

$7 + \frac{1}{5} \div 2 = \boxed{}$

c.

$2 \div \frac{1}{5} \div 6 = \boxed{}$

d.

$8 - \frac{1}{4} \div 3 = \boxed{}$

2. Solve each problem. Show your thinking.

a. A rectangular picture measures $3\frac{1}{2}$ ft by $4\frac{1}{4}$ ft. It will be framed with strips of lumber that are $\frac{1}{4}$ of a foot wide. What will be the perimeter of the framed picture?

$\boxed{}$ ft

b. Daniel is tiling around the border of a courtyard that is 3.6 yd wide and 4.5 yd long. He is using tiles that are 1 ft by 1 ft. About how many tiles will he need to buy?

$\boxed{}$ tiles

Preparing for Module 12

Use factors or a partitioning strategy to divide. Show your thinking.

a.

$756 \div 18 = \boxed{}$

b.

$1,272 \div 24 = \boxed{}$

Step In

The local library is having new carpet installed in a reading room. This diagram shows the dimensions of the space to be covered.

How much space will be covered by the new carpet?

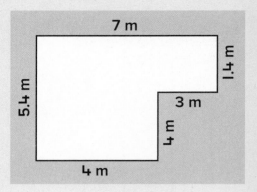

The space could be split into two rectangles.

Gabriel figured it out like this.

Explain the steps he used. Color the diagram to show the area of Rectangle A.

Rectangle A	Rectangle B	Whole Shape
$A = L \times W$	$A = L \times W$	$A = 21.6 + 4.2$
$A = 5.4 \times 4$	$A = 3 \times 1.4$	$A = 25.8$ m²
$A = 21.6$ m²	$A = 4.2$ m²	

Is there another way to calculate the area?

Step Up

1. Use the centimeter rulers to calculate the area of this rectangle. Show your thinking.

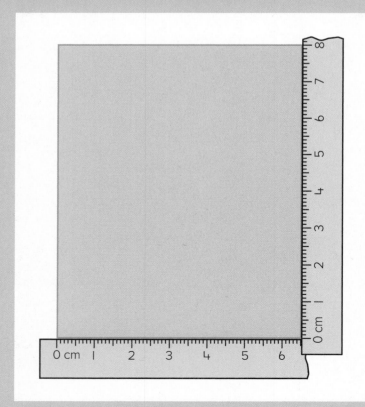

Area _____

2. Solve each problem. Show your thinking. Remember to write the unit of measurement.

a. Ashley's bedroom is 4.3 yards long and 3 yards wide. Grace's bedroom is 12 feet long and 15 feet wide. What is the difference in area?

b. Each side of Beatrice's square chicken coop is 3.6 meters long. She decides to extend one pair of opposite sides by 350 cm each. By how much did she increase the area of her coop?

c. Tama's house has a rectangular patio that is 6 yards long by 9 feet wide. He is building an extension that will make the total area of the patio 35 yd². What is the area of the extension he is building?

d. A rectangular riding arena is 45 meters long. The stables are 10 meters wide and 26.6 meters long. The total area of the arena and stables is 986 m². What is the width of the riding arena?

Step Ahead   Calculate the total area of this shape. Show your thinking.

Step In

Aston bought this storage crate. It is 15.75 inches long by 12 inches wide. How much floor space will the crate take up?

How can you calculate the area?

Teena figured it out like this.

A = Area of base

$A = L \times W$

$A = 15.75 \times 12$

$A = 189$ in²

The volume of the crate is 9,450 in³.
How could you calculate the height of the crate?

> Volume = base × height. I know the base and the volume. I don't know the height, so 189 × H = 9,450 in³.

How could you use division to calculate the unknown part?

Step Up

1. This box of staples is 3 centimeters high. Its base is shown below. Use the measurements shown to calculate the volume of the box. Show your thinking.

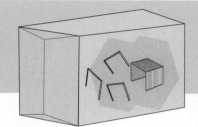

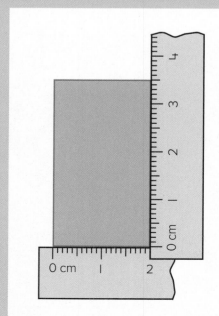

Volume [   ]

2. Solve each problem. Show your thinking. Remember to write the unit of measurement.

a. Nathan and his friend rent a storage unit for one month. They share the cost and space equally. The unit is 6 ft by 12 ft by 10 ft. How much space is available for each person?

b. A gift box measures 4.5 cm wide by 2.5 cm deep. Its height is the sum of the width and depth. The gift has a volume of 50 cm³. After the gift has been packed in the box how much space inside the box is not used?

c. Suitcase A is 2.5 feet long, 2 feet wide, and 2 feet high. Suitcase B is 36 inches long, 24 inches wide, and 18 inches high. What is the difference in volume?

d. Bianca is building a sandbox that will hold 4 cubic yards of sand. She wants it to be 18 inches deep and 2 yards wide. What will be the length?

Step Ahead

Draw and label the length, width, and height of a container that matches all these clues.

CLUES

- I am a square-based prism.
- My volume is 468 in³.
- The area of my base is 36 in².
- My dimensions are all whole numbers.

Think and Solve

The numbers in the circles are the sums of the rows and the columns.

Same shapes and letters are the same numbers.

△	■	⬡	E	F

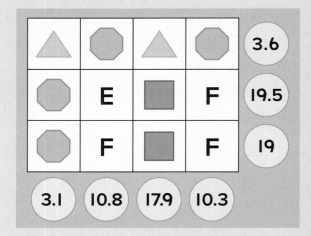

Words at Work

Write in words how you solve this problem.

Owen is packing boxes in a storage unit. Each box has a square base that is 15 inches wide. Each box is 40 inches tall. The storage unit is 5 ft wide × 5 ft long × 6 ft high. The boxes can be stored upright or lying on a side to fit the floor space. What is the greatest number of these boxes Owen can fit in the storage unit? How much space is left over?

1. Solve each problem. Show your thinking.

a. Dad cuts $\frac{3}{4}$ yard of hose into 2 equal pieces. How long is each piece?

☐ yd

FROM 5.9.7

b. In a Kindergarten relay, 4 runners each run the same distance to complete the $\frac{2}{3}$ mile race. How far did each child run?

☐ mi

2. Solve each problem. Show your thinking.

a. A rectangular swimming pool is 25 meters long, 12 meters wide, and 1.8 meters deep. What is the volume of the pool?

☐ m³

FROM 5.11.12

b. Each side of a square cake tin measures 20 cm. The tin has a volume of 3,000 cm³. How deep is the cake tin?

☐ cm

Preparing for Module 12

Calculate the monthly payments for each phone. Then draw a ✔ beside the plan that is the best value.

a.

$384

paid over
6 months

$_____ each month

b.

$574

paid over
7 months

$_____ each month

c.

$424

paid over
8 months

$_____ each month

Step In

Three people share the cost of renting this car.

How could you calculate each person's share?

Natalie showed the total cost with blocks, then followed these steps to figure out each share.

	Step 1	Step 2	Step 3
	Share the hundreds.	Share the tens.	Share the ones.
Shares			

Dwane followed these steps to help him write the amount in each share.

	Step 1	Step 2	Step 3
	Share the hundreds.	Share the tens.	Share the ones.
Shares	100	100 + 10	100 + 10 + 6
	100	100 + 10	100 + 10 + 6
	100	100 + 10	100 + 10 + 6

How much is each person's share of the car rental?

Step Up

1. Draw a different quantity of hundreds, tens, and ones blocks that can be used to calculate 452 ÷ 4.

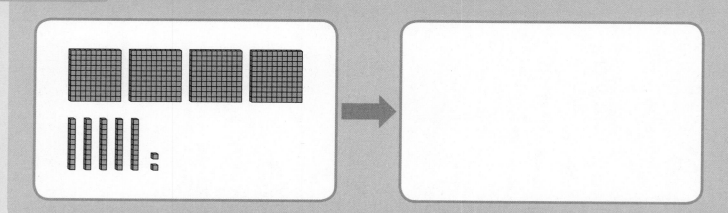

2. Calculate the amount in each share. You can use blocks to help your thinking.

a.
$$\$512 \div 4 = \text{_____}$$
$\$\underline{\hspace{2cm}}$

100
100
100
100

b.
$$\$798 \div 6 = \text{_____}$$
$\$\underline{\hspace{2cm}}$

c.
$$\$645 \div 5 = \text{_____}$$
$\$\underline{\hspace{2cm}}$

3. Calculate these. Use blocks to help. Show your thinking.

a.
$$375 \div 3 = \text{_____}$$

b.
$$528 \div 4 = \text{_____}$$

c.
$$4{,}206 \div 3 = \text{_____}$$

d.
$$3{,}205 \div 5 = \text{_____}$$

Step Ahead

For both of these, write a digit to complete a three-digit number that you can divide without any amount left over. Then write the quotients.

a.
5 8 □ ÷ 3 = _____

b.
6 2 □ ÷ 5 = _____

Step In

Four people shared the cost of a restaurant bill for $84.

Gloria calculated each share and recorded her thinking like this.

How much did each person pay?

4 people share $84
2 tens + 1 one
2 tens + 1 one
2 tens + 1 one
2 tens + 1 one

Another way to record the calculation is to use a division bracket.

What numbers are written around this division bracket?
What does each number tell you?

$$4 \overline{)84}$$

What is happening in each of these steps?

How are the steps similar to Gloria's method?

Step 1
T O
2
4)‾ 8 ‾ 4

Step 2
T O
2 1
4)‾ 8 ‾ 4

Look at these steps to figure out 906 shared by 3.

Step 1
H T O
3
3)‾ 9 ‾ 0 ‾ 6

Step 2
H T O
3 0
3)‾ 9 ‾ 0 ‾ 6

Step 3
H T O
3 0 2
3)‾ 9 ‾ 0 ‾ 6

What is happening in each step?

Why is 0 written above the bracket in Step 2?

I think I could skip Step 1 because I know that 90 tens divided by 3 is 30 tens.

> Numbers in equations are arranged in different positions when using division brackets.
>
> $64 \div 2 = 32$ $2 \overline{)64}$ = 32

1. Rewrite each equation using the division bracket.

a.

$68 \div 2 = 34$

T O

b.

$32 = 96 \div 3$

T O

c.

$412 = 824 \div 2$

H T O

d.

$309 \div 3 = 103$

H T O

2. Use the steps on page 436 to calculate each quotient.

a.

T O

2) 8 2

b.

H T O

3) 6 9 3

c.

Th H T O

2) 8 6 2 6

d.

3) 6 3

e.

4) 8 0 4

f.

4) 4 0 4 8

g.

4) 8 4

h.

2) 4 6 0

i.

3) 9 3 0 9

3. Choose three problems from Question 2. Rewrite each as an equation.

Write digits to complete each problem.

a.

Th H T O

  1 3 2 0

3)   9

b.

Th H T O

  3 4 0

) 6 8   2

Computation Practice

What's big, white, furry, and found in the Grand Canyon?

★ Complete the equations. Then write each letter above its matching answer at the bottom of the page.

$3.48 ÷ 4 = $ _____   **r** $8.40 ÷ 5 = $ _____   **o**

5 × $3.15 = $ _____   **l**   4 × $5.50 = $ _____   **a**

$6.24 ÷ 4 = $ _____   **a** $7.20 ÷ 3 = $ _____   **y**

$6.50 × 4 = $ _____   **s** $2.25 × 3 = $ _____   **e**

$7.50 ÷ 5 = $ _____   **a** $8.70 ÷ 3 = $ _____   **r**

$5.25 × 4 = $ _____   **t**   5 × $4.49 = $ _____   **o**

$6.60 ÷ 3 = $ _____   **b** $9.75 ÷ 5 = $ _____   **v**

5 × $3.20 = $ _____   **l** $4.30 × 4 = $ _____   **p**

$4.80 ÷ 4 = $ _____   **r**   3 × $3.15 = $ _____   **e**

$22.00 $1.95 $6.75 $0.87 $2.40 $16.00 $1.68 $26.00 $21.00

$17.20 $22.45 $15.75 $1.50 $1.20 $2.20 $9.45 $1.56 $2.90

I. Rewrite each equation with common fractions.
Then calculate the product.

a.
$7 \times 0.4 =$ ⬜

b.
$6 \times 0.08 =$ ⬜

c.
$0.03 \times 9 =$ ⬜

d.
$0.8 \times 8 =$ ⬜

e.
$9 \times 0.7 =$ ⬜

f.
$0.09 \times 6 =$ ⬜

2. Rewrite each equation using the division bracket.

a.
$72 \div 3 = 24$

T O

b.
$21 = 84 \div 4$

T O

c.
$107 = 535 \div 5$

H T O

d.
$408 \div 4 = 102$

H T O

Preparing for Next Year

Read the number on the expander. Then round each number to the nearest **whole number**, **tenth**, and **hundredth**.

	Nearest Whole Number	Nearest Tenth	Nearest Hundredth

a.

b.

c.

Step In Three friends equally share $78.

Liam used blocks and wrote this to figure out each share.

How much is each share?

What regrouping did Liam have to do? How do you know?

$$78 \div 3$$
$$7 \text{ tens} \div 3 = 2 \text{ tens}$$
$$\text{and I ten left over}$$
$$18 \text{ ones} \div 3 = 6 \text{ ones}$$

Terri tried using the division bracket but did not know how to show the regrouping.

```
      T   O
      2
3 ) 7   8
```

Reece showed her the standard division algorithm to help.

Step I	
Divide	T · O
There are 7 tens to share. There are 3 shares. There are 2 tens in each share because 3 × 2 is 6.	3) 7 | 8 (2 above 7)

Step 2	
Multiply then subtract.	T · O
There are 7 tens to share. There are 6 tens shared. There is I ten left over because 7 − 6 is I.	3) 7 | 8, − 6, I

Step 3	
There is I ten left to share. There are 8 ones to share. That makes 18 ones to share.	3) 7 | 8, − 6, I ↓ 8

Reece completed the standard algorithm by repeating the first two steps with 18 ones.

```
      T   O
      2   6
3 ) 7   8
  - 6   ↓
      I   8
    - I   8
          0
```

How is Reece's method similar to Liam's method?

What is another method you could use?

Use the standard division algorithm to calculate 68 ÷ 4.

Step Up

Use the standard division algorithm to calculate each quotient. Remember to estimate before or after your calculation to check your accuracy.

a.
```
   T   O
4 ) 5   6
```

b.
```
   T   O
3 ) 8   1
```

c.
```
   T   O
5 ) 8   5
```

d.
```
   T   O
2 ) 7   6
```

e.
```
6 ) 8   4
```

f.
```
3 ) 7   8
```

g.
```
7 ) 9   1
```

h.
```
3 ) 5   4
```

i.
```
8 ) 9   6
```

j.
```
4 ) 9   2
```

k.
```
5 ) 7   5
```

l.
```
3 ) 4   8
```

Step Ahead

Show two different ways to calculate 87 ÷ 3.

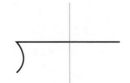

Step In

A rope that is 645 centimeters long is cut into three equal parts.

How would you calculate the length of each part?

Lisa decided to use the standard division algorithm to calculate each length.

What steps has she completed?
What does she need to do next?

Complete Lisa's calculation.

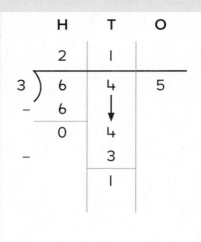

Four wheels cost \$832. How much does each wheel cost?

Ruben followed these steps to figure it out.

8 hundreds divided by 4	3 tens divided by 4	32 ones divided by 4
2 hundreds	2 hundreds + 0 tens	2 hundreds + 0 tens + 8 ones
2 hundreds	2 hundreds + 0 tens	2 hundreds + 0 tens + 8 ones
2 hundreds	2 hundreds + 0 tens	2 hundreds + 0 tens + 8 ones
2 hundreds	2 hundreds + 0 tens	2 hundreds + 0 tens + 8 ones

Ruth and Jamar both used the standard algorithm.

Compare their calculations.

What do you notice about the steps Jamar used?

Why do you think he worked with the 3 tens and 2 ones at the same time?

Did this affect the final answer?

How does each method relate to Ruben's method?

Ruth

	H	T	O
	2	0	8
4)	8	3	2
–	8		
	0	3	
–		0	
		3	2
–		3	2
			0

Jamar

	H	T	O
	2	0	8
4)	8	3	2
–	8		
	0	3	2
–		3	2
			0

Complete these calculations using the standard division algorithm.

a.

H	T	O

3) 4　8　6

b.

H	T	O

4) 9　0　4

c.

H	T	O

5) 4　1　5

d.

4) 6　1　8　4

e.

6) 1　8　7　2

f.

5) 3　2　0　5

Step Ahead

Choose two problems above that you can solve easily **without** using the standard division algorithm. Show your methods.

Think and Solve

Selena has a box containing pencils, pens, and markers.

- For every 5 pencils, she has 3 pens.
- For every marker, she has 6 pens.
- There is a total of 68 pens, pencils, and markers in Selena's box.

a. How many markers are in the box? _____

b. How many pens are in the box? _____

c. How many pencils are in the box? _____

Words at Work

Imagine another student was away from school when you learned the steps of the division algorithm. Write the steps you would use to teach the student how to complete this example.

$$6 \overline{)\ 9 \quad 6}$$

Ongoing Practice

I. Use the partial-products strategy to calculate each product. Show your thinking.

a.

9 × 0.27 = _____

b.

0.54 × 7 = _____

c.

6 × 0.38 = _____

d.

0.45 × 8 = _____

e.

5 × 0.29 = _____

f.

0.75 × 4 = _____

2. Complete these calculations using the standard division algorithm.

a.

	H	T	O
3)	7	2	6

b.

	H	T	O
4)	9	7	6

c.

	H	T	O
5)	8	5	5

Preparing for Next Year   Calculate the total cost of each purchase. Show your thinking.

a.

○ $4.95   ○ $5.47

$ _____

b.

○ $13.98   ○ $2.39

$ _____

Division: Working with the standard algorithm (with remainders)

Step In

Muffins are sold in boxes of five. There are 267 muffins to pack.

Will there be any muffins left over?
How do you know?

> I know there will be some muffins left over because there is no 0 or 5 in the ones place.

How many boxes of muffins can be sold?

Connor used the standard division algorithm.

Describe the steps that he used.

How many boxes are needed?
How many muffins are remaining?
How is the remainder recorded?
How could you record the remainder as a common fraction?

How could you pack 267 muffins in boxes of a different size so there are no muffins left over?

		H	T	O	
			5	3	R2
5	)	2	6	7	
	−	2	5	↓	
			1	7	
	−		1	5	
				2	

Step Up

1. Complete these calculations using the standard division algorithm. Record the remainder as a whole number.

a.

H	T	O	
			R
5) 6	3	7	

b.

H	T	O	
			R
3) 2	0	9	

c.

H	T	O	
			R
4) 6	5	5	

2. Solve each problem, writing an answer that makes sense of the remainder.
Show your thinking.

a. 5 sheets of paper are used in one booklet.
There are 582 sheets of paper.
How many whole booklets can be made?

_____ booklets

b. Blake's pool can hold 2,539 gal of water when full. If it takes 9 hours to fill the empty pool, how much water will be in the pool after 1 hour?

gal

c. 6 pencils are packed into each box.
There are 3,620 pencils to pack.
How many pencils will be left over?

_____ pencils

d. Brooklyn Bridge is 5,989 ft long and 85 ft wide. What distance is one-sixth of its length?

ft

Step Ahead   Write an equation that includes a four-digit dividend and leaves a remainder of 3.

Step In

Rita plans to buy a used car from a friend for $6,560. She will make 40 equal payments to pay the total cost.

How could you calculate the amount of each payment?

Jacob used the standard division algorithm. He started like this.

What has he done in this part of his calculation?

Why do you think he did that?

6 thousands blocks can't be divided into 40 parts, so he regrouped the 6 thousands as hundreds from the start.

	Th	H	T	O
		1		
40)	6	5	6	0
−	4	0		
	2	5		

What has he done in this part of his calculation?

Why did he write 240 on the fourth line under the division bracket?

He needed to divide 256 tens by 40. What did he multiply 40 by to make a product close to 256?

	Th	H	T	O
		1	6	
40)	6	5	6	0
−	4	0	↓	
	2	5	6	
−	2	4	0	
		1	6	

Complete Jacob's calculation.

Vishaya decided to break 6,560 into parts to divide.

How do you think she split the number?

She might have split it so one part was 4,000. That would be an easy way to start.

I. Complete each equation.

a.
[ ] × 50 = 3,500

so 3,500 ÷ 50 = [ ]

b.
[ ] × 40 = 3,200

so 3,200 ÷ 40 = [ ]

c.
[ ] × 70 = 2,100

so 2,100 ÷ 70 = [ ]

2. Use a method of your choice to solve each problem. Show your thinking.

a.
4,290 ÷ 30 = [ ]

b.
4,250 ÷ 50 = [ ]

c.
5,760 ÷ 30 = [ ]

d.
7,590 ÷ 30 = [ ]

e.
7,560 ÷ 60 = [ ]

f.
5,720 ÷ 40 = [ ]

Step Ahead

Write the missing numbers on this trail.

60 → × 4 → [ ] → × 10 → [ ] → ÷ 40 → [ ]

Computation Practice   What flies all day but never goes anywhere?

⭐ Complete the equations. Find each product in the grid below and cross out the letter above. Then write the remaining letters at the bottom of the page.

$1.75 × 3 = $_____

4 × $1.95 = $_____

3 × $2.65 = $_____

4 × $1.65 = $_____

$1.15 × 5 = $_____

$1.35 × 3 = $_____

$3.15 × 3 = $_____

4 × $2.45 = $_____

5 × $1.85 = $_____

4 × $2.25 = $_____

$1.55 × 3 = $_____

$1.25 × 5 = $_____

$1.55 × 5 = $_____

5 × $1.45 = $_____

4 × $2.15 = $_____

5 × $1.95 = $_____

$2.25 × 3 = $_____

$1.75 × 4 = $_____

$2.45 × 3 = $_____

A	S	A	N	D	F	L	Y
$5.25	$6.25	$4.55	$9.45	$7.75	$7.05	$9.75	$6.60
F	L	I	E	S	B	E	E
$7.35	$4.15	$7.80	$9.80	$6.75	$7.95	$7.25	$9.25
G	N	A	T	P	I	G	S
$5.75	$7.00	$5.95	$4.65	$8.60	$4.05	$9.55	$9.00

Write the letters in order from the ✳ to the bottom-right corner.

☐ ☐☐☐☐

Ongoing Practice

1. Calculate the area of each room. Show your thinking.

a. Bedroom 3.2 m by 4.1 m

_____ m²

b. Bedroom 2.8 m by 2.4 m

_____ m²

2. Use the standard algorithm to calculate each quotient. Record the remainder as a whole number.

a.

Th	H	T	O	
				R

6) 3 6 3 9

b.

Th	H	T	O	
				R

3) 4 9 2 8

c.

Th	H	T	O	
				R

4) 3 4 1 8

Preparing for Next Year

Calculate the difference in mass between these sacks of grain. Show your thinking.

a. 15.35 kg   7.6 kg

_____ kg

b. 4.25 kg   12.1 kg

_____ kg

c. 3.85 kg   7.12 kg

_____ kg

Step In   Morgan plans to buys some kitchen appliances for $3,012.
She will make 12 equal payments to pay the total cost.

How could you calculate the amount she must pay each month?

Describe each of these methods.

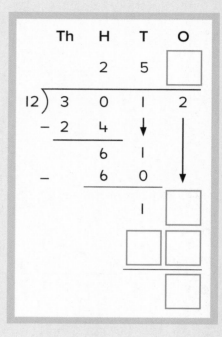

$3,012 \div 12$

$2,400 \div 12 = 200$
$600 \div 12 = 50$
$12 \div 12 = \underline{1}$
251

$3,012 \div 12$

is the same value as

$1,506 \div 6$

is the same value as

$753 \div 3$

Antonio used the standard division algorithm.

He started like this.
What did he do in this part of his calculation?

Write numbers in each empty box to complete the algorithm.

Think about the three different methods that were used to solve this
problem. Which strategy do you prefer? Why?

Step Up   1.   Complete these calculations using the standard division algorithm.

© ORIGO Education

2. Use a method of your choice to solve each problem. Show your thinking.

a.
$2,280 \div 15 =$ _____

b.
$7,640 \div 20 =$ _____

c.
$5,000 \div 40 =$ _____

d.
$8,175 \div 25 =$ _____

e.
$3,840 \div 12 =$ _____

f.
$4,097 \div 17 =$ _____

Step Ahead

Dorothy used this strategy to figure out the answer to Question 2c. Do you think her strategy is correct? Explain your thinking.

$5,000 \div 40$
is the same value as
$500 \div 4$

Step In

Kazem's college books cost $379.20.

He made equal payments over one year to pay for the books.

About how much did he pay each month?

How would you calculate the exact amount?

Susan changed the decimal fraction to a whole number.

$$37,920 \div 12$$
$$36,000 \div 12 = 3,000$$
$$1,200 \div 12 = \quad 100$$
$$720 \div 12 = \quad \underline{60}$$
$$3,160$$

$$3,160 \div 100 = 31.60$$

Jerome used the standard division algorithm.

```
           3   1 . 6   0
    12 ) 3  7   9 . 2   0
       - 3  6   ↓
            1   9
       -    1   2
                7   2
            -   7   2
                    0   0
```

What steps did each person follow? Which strategy do you prefer?

How did Susan change the decimal fraction into a whole number?

How did she adjust the answer afterward?

Step Up

1. Calculate each monthly payment. Show your thinking.

a.
5 equal payments   ○ **$709.20**

$_____

b.
9 equal payments   ○ **$470.52**

$_____

2. Solve each problem. Show your thinking.

a. Amber's new phone costs $673.50. 15 equal monthly payments are made to pay for the phone. How much does she pay each month?

$_____

b. Robert has $45 in savings. Jennifer has $810 saved. How many times greater is Jennifer's savings compared to Robert's savings?

_____ times

c. A large box contains 14 items and weighs 115.2 kg. This is 6 times heavier than a small box which contains 8 items. How much does the small box weigh?

_____ kg

d. A cycle race is 216.9 km long. Drink stations are located every 35 km. What is the distance from the final station to the finish line?

_____ km

Step Ahead

Calculate each cost then color the ⬭ beside the better buy. Show your thinking.

Chairs	**Chairs**
⬭ 12 for $401.40	⬭ 15 for $467.40

Think and Solve

a. Try to write two whole numbers in parts A to G of this diagram.

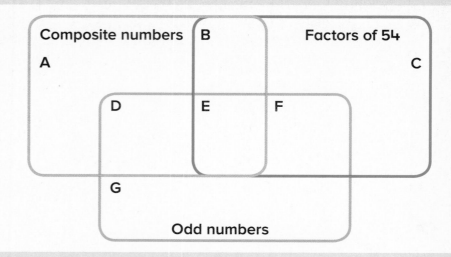

Composite numbers

A

B

Factors of 54

C

D

E

F

G

Odd numbers

b. Write what you notice.

Words at Work

Write about a situation where you might need to divide a four- or five-digit dividend by a two-digit divisor.

Ongoing Practice

1. Complete each equation. Remember to write the quotient as a decimal fraction. Show your thinking.

a.

$0.6 \div 2 = \rule{2cm}{0.4pt}$

b.

$0.12 \div 3 = \rule{2cm}{0.4pt}$

c.

$0.4 \div 8 = \rule{2cm}{0.4pt}$

d.

$0.35 \div 7 = \rule{2cm}{0.4pt}$

e.

$0.18 \div 6 = \rule{2cm}{0.4pt}$

f.

$0.40 \div 20 = \rule{2cm}{0.4pt}$

2. Complete each equation. Show your thinking.

a.

$2{,}870 \div 14 = \rule{2cm}{0.4pt}$

b.

$2{,}016 \div 16 = \rule{2cm}{0.4pt}$

Preparing for Next Year

Write the products. Color or outline parts of the squares to show your thinking. Each large square is one whole.

a.

$5 \times 0.05 = \rule{2cm}{0.4pt}$

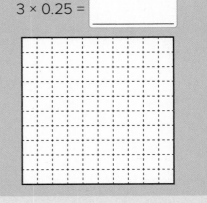

b.

$4 \times 0.12 = \rule{2cm}{0.4pt}$

c.

$3 \times 0.25 = \rule{2cm}{0.4pt}$

Step In   Four friends share the cost of this gift.

$50

About how much money should each person pay?

$10 is not enough and $15 is too much.
The amount that each person pays must
be somewhere between these two amounts.

At a restaurant, three friends equally share the cost of this meal.

About how much should each person pay?

How did you form your estimate?

The total cost is about $70, so I would
probably ask each person to pay $25.
I would then share the change.

Table 24	
I steak	$21.95
I fish	$20.50
I burger	$18.90
3 sodas	$ 9.00

Step Up

1. Estimate the amount that each person pays. Make sure there is enough
   money to pay for the purchase. Show your thinking.

a. 5 friends share $19.80

Estimate $_____

b. 3 friends share $47.05

Estimate $_____

c. 7 friends share $32.50

Estimate $_____

d. 4 friends share $58.95

Estimate $_____

2. Estimate the total cost. Then calculate the approximate amount that each person pays. Show your thinking.

a.
4 friends share ⬡ ○ **$18.95** ⬡ ○ **$61.15**

Estimate $_____

b.
5 friends share ⬡ ○ **$14.98** ⬡ ○ **$20.50**

Estimate $_____

c.
10 friends share ⬡ ○ **$19.00** ⬡ ○ **$30.90**

Estimate $_____

d.
7 friends share ⬡ ○ **$28.04** ⬡ ○ **$50.10**

Estimate $_____

3. Estimate the answer to each problem. Show your thinking.

a. Patricia rides her bike a similar distance each day. In 5 days she rides 50.1 miles. About how far does she ride each day?

_____ mi

b. A rope is 19.79 meters long. Ben cuts it in half. He then cuts each half into 3 equal pieces. About how long is each piece of rope?

_____ m

Step Ahead

Use the cost of buying 6 CDs to estimate the cost of buying 8 CDs. Explain how you formed your estimate.

_____

_____

_____

CD Pack 6 — 6 for **$55.95**

CD Pack 8 — 8 for $_____

Step In

How can you split the cost of this meal equally among four people?

You could break $24.20 into dollars and cents. This diagram makes the division easier.

How much is each person's share?

What fraction of one dollar is one cent?

How would you write that as a decimal fraction?

What fraction of one dollar is five cents?

How would you write that as a decimal fraction?

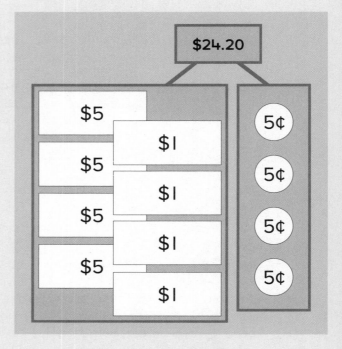

$24.20

$5	$1	5¢
$5	$1	5¢
$5	$1	5¢
$5	$1	5¢

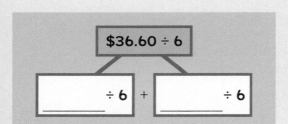

$36.60 ÷ 6

_____ ÷ 6 + _____ ÷ 6

Complete this diagram to show how you could break $36.60 into two parts to make it easier to divide by 6.

What is the answer?

Step Up

1. Complete the parts, and then write the answer.

a. $8.60 ÷ 4 **is the same value as** $_____ ÷ 4 plus _____¢ ÷ 4 = $_____

b. $15.50 ÷ 5 **is the same value as** $_____ ÷ 5 plus _____¢ ÷ 5 = $_____

c. $12.90 ÷ 6 **is the same value as** $_____ ÷ 6 plus _____¢ ÷ 6 = $_____

d. $18.60 ÷ 3 **is the same value as** $_____ ÷ 3 plus _____¢ ÷ 3 = $_____

2. Calculate each share. Then complete the equations.

a.

Share ○$63.30 by 3.

$_____ ÷ _____ = $_____

_____¢ ÷ _____ = _____¢

Each share is

$_____

b.

Share ○$32.80 by 4.

$_____ ÷ _____ = $_____

_____¢ ÷ _____ = _____¢

Each share is

$_____

c.

Share ○$54.60 by 6.

$_____ ÷ _____ = $_____

_____¢ ÷ _____ = _____¢

Each share is

$_____

3. Complete each equation. Show your thinking.

a.
12.60 ÷ 3 = _____

b.
48.60 ÷ 2 = _____

c.
36.60 ÷ 3 = _____

d.
28.08 ÷ 4 = _____

e.
50.10 ÷ 5 = _____

f.
16.20 ÷ 4 = _____

Step Ahead

Three friends decide to contribute equal amounts to buy a soccer ball. How much **less** will they each have to pay if a fourth person contributes?

$_____ less

$24.60

Computation Practice

Which month has 28 days each year and 29 days every leap year?

★ Complete the equations. Then find each answer in the puzzle below and shade the matching letter. The remaining letters will spell the answer.

$21 - 9.6 =$ ____	$37.7 + 0.8 =$ ____	$20.3 - 6.8 =$ ____
$9.7 + 21.6 =$ ____	$25.1 - 9.6 =$ ____	$25.1 + 9.6 =$ ____
$17.4 - 8.7 =$ ____	$9.6 + 6.9 =$ ____	$14.8 - 7.9 =$ ____
$7.9 + 14.8 =$ ____	$35 - 10.8 =$ ____	$0.9 + 20.9 =$ ____
$26.1 - 0.8 =$ ____	$3.3 + 7.7 =$ ____	$42 - 8.6 =$ ____
$13.5 + 18.6 =$ ____	$18.6 - 13.7 =$ ____	$6.8 + 20.3 =$ ____
$9.6 - 6.9 =$ ____	$8.7 + 17.4 =$ ____	$25.1 - 7.6 =$ ____

Ongoing Practice

1. Write a multiplication equation to solve each division problem.
Then write the quotient.

a.

6.3 ÷ 0.9 = ☐

_____

b.

3.6 ÷ 0.4 = ☐

_____

c.

5.6 ÷ 0.7 = ☐

_____

d.

5.4 ÷ 0.6 = ☐

_____

e.

4.8 ÷ 0.8 = ☐

_____

f.

8.1 ÷ 0.9 = ☐

_____

2. Calculate each monthly payment. Show your thinking.

a. 6 equal monthly payments   ◯ **$162.60**

$ _____

b. 9 equal monthly payments   ◯ **$709.20**

$ _____

Preparing for Next Year

Write a multiplication equation to calculate the area of each part.
Then write the total area.

20

8

40   1

28 × 41		
_____ × _____	=	_____
_____ × _____	=	_____
_____ × _____	=	_____
_____ × _____	=	_____
	Total	_____

Step In

Six students equally share the cost of this gift. How much will they each pay?

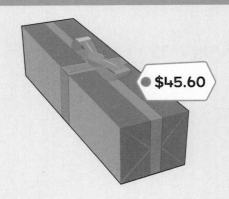

● $45.60

I can split $45.60 into two parts that are easier to divide.

How many of the whole dollars can be shared by 6?
How much remains to be shared?

Complete this diagram to show how you would split $45.60 into two parts that are easier to divide by 6.

Is there another way you could divide?

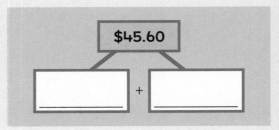

$45.60

[   ] + [   ]

Step Up

1. Break each number into parts that you can easily divide. Calculate the partial quotients. Then complete the equations.

a.

$22.50 ÷ 3 = $_____

[   ] ÷ 3 = _____ + [   ] ÷ 3 = _____

b.

$34.40 ÷ 8 = $_____

[   ] ÷ 8 = _____ + [   ] ÷ 8 = _____

c.

$27.60 ÷ 6 = $_____

[   ] ÷ 6 = _____ + [   ] ÷ 6 = _____

d.

$28.80 ÷ 9 = $_____

[   ] ÷ 9 = _____ + [   ] ÷ 9 = _____

e.

$52.80 ÷ 8 = $_____

[   ] ÷ 8 = _____ + [   ] ÷ 8 = _____

f.

$34.80 ÷ 4 = $_____

[   ] ÷ 4 = _____ + [   ] ÷ 4 = _____

© ORIGO Education

2. Calculate the quotients. Show your thinking.

a.
44.70 ÷ 3 = _____

b.
37.60 ÷ 4 = _____

c.
48.60 ÷ 9 = _____

d.
37.10 ÷ 7 = _____

e.
25.20 ÷ 3 = _____

f.
14.40 ÷ 4 = _____

g.
58.40 ÷ 8 = _____

h.
39.60 ÷ 6 = _____

i.
46.90 ÷ 7 = _____

Step Ahead

Four students each contribute $8.40 to buy a gift for their teacher. Three more students decide to contribute toward the same gift. How much will each student have to pay now?

$ _____

Working Space

Step In

Look at these pack prices.

6 for **$3.96** — Rulers

4 for **$6.80** — Blank CDs

8 for **$5.92** — Notebooks

How do store owners decide the prices for packs like these?

How could you calculate the cost of a single item in each pack?

I could split the total cost of the rulers into two amounts that are easier to work with like this.

$3.96 ÷ 6
$3.60 ÷ 6 = 60¢
36¢ ÷ 6 = 6¢
_____
66¢

How could you split the total cost of the CDs to make the division easier?

Paige split the total cost of the notebooks like this.

$4 + $1.60 + 32¢

Is there another way?

Step Up

1. Calculate the cost of a single item in each pack. Show your thinking.

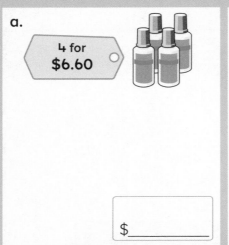

a. 4 for **$6.60**

$_____

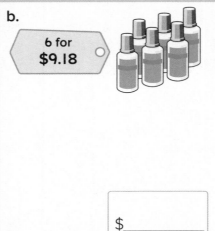

b. 6 for **$9.18**

$_____

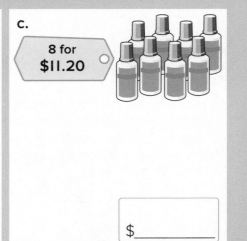

c. 8 for **$11.20**

$_____

2. Identical products are being sold. Color the ◯ beside the better offer.
Show the steps you use to figure it out.

a. Raffle Tickets
◯ 4 for $5.20

Raffle Tickets
◯ 5 for $7.15

b. Baseball Cards
◯ 6 for $8.40

Baseball Cards
◯ 9 for $9.95

c. Orange Juice
◯ 4 for $2.96

Orange Juice
◯ 6 for $3.30

d. Granola Bars
◯ 5 for $4.30

Granola Bars
◯ 8 for $6.92

3. Yuma is printing some photos. 6 photos cost $3.90 to print. It costs $2 more to print
10 photos. Which offer is the better value for money?

_____ photos for $ _____

Step Ahead

Look at this special deal
on packs of soda.

SODA
Buy 4 packs get
one pack free

PACK OF 12
SODA CANS

$4.92

a. If you buy one pack of 12 cans,
what is the cost of a single can? _____ ¢

b. If you buy four packs, you get one pack free.
Calculate the cost of a single can if you buy
four packs.

Round the cost to the nearest cent. _____ ¢

© ORIGO Education

Think and Solve

Same shapes are the same number of kilograms.

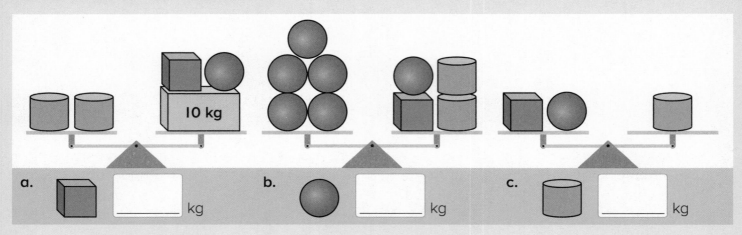

a. _____ kg

b. _____ kg

c. _____ kg

Words at Work

Write about two different methods you could use to calculate $96.72 ÷ 8.

Ongoing Practice

1. Write an equation to represent each problem. Use a letter for the unknown amount. Then calculate the answer. Show your thinking.

a. Amy is making some new cushions. Each cushion uses 0.8 yards of fabric. She has 6.4 yards of fabric. How many cushions can she make?

_____ cushions

b. A muffin recipe uses 0.07 kilograms of yogurt. How much yogurt is needed to make 6 batches of the muffins?

_____ kg

2. Complete each equation. Show your thinking.

a. $\$33.60 \div 3 = \$$_____

b. $\$32.80 \div 4 = \$$_____

c. $\$35.55 \div 5 = \$$_____

Preparing for Next Year

Graph the coordinates from the table on the coordinate plane.

x (Input)	1	4	3	6
y (Output)	2	5	4	7

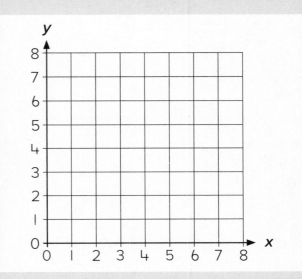

Algorithm

Algorithms are rules used for completing tasks or for solving problems. There are standard algorithms for calculating answers for addition, subtraction, multiplication and division problems. This example shows the division algorithm.

$$
\begin{array}{c|c|c|c}
 & 2 & 0 & 8 \\
\hline
4\overline{)} & 8 & 3 & 2 \\
- & 8 & \downarrow & \downarrow \\
\hline
 & 0 & 3 & 2 \\
- & & 3 & 2 \\
\hline
 & & & 0
\end{array}
$$

Area

Area is the amount of surface that a shape covers. This amount is usually described in square units such as square centimeters (cm^2) or square inches (in^2).

Capacity

Customary Units of Capacity		Metric Units of Capacity	
8 fluid ounces (fl oz)	1 cup (c)	1,000 milliliters (mL)	1 liter (L)
2 cups	1 pint (pt)		
2 pints	1 quart (qt)		
4 quarts	1 gallon (gal)		

Common fraction

$\frac{2}{3}$ is shaded

Fractions describe equal parts of a whole. In this common fraction, 2 is the numerator and 3 is the denominator.

The denominator shows the total number of equal parts (3). The numerator shows the number of those parts (2).

A **common denominator** is one that two or more fractions have in common.

Equivalent fractions are fractions that cover the same amount of area on a shape or are located on the same point on a number line.

For example: $\frac{1}{2}$ is equivalent to $\frac{2}{4}$.

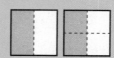
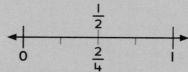

Proper fractions are common fractions that have a numerator that is less than the denominator. For example, $\frac{2}{5}$ is a proper fraction.

Improper fractions are common fractions that have a numerator that is greater than or equal to the denominator. For example, $\frac{7}{5}$ and $\frac{4}{4}$ are improper fractions.

A **mixed number** is an improper fraction that has been changed to show the whole part/s and the fractional part. For example, $\frac{13}{6}$ is equivalent to $2\frac{1}{6}$.

Coordinate plane

A **coordinate plane** is a rectangular grid which has a horizontal axis called the *x*-axis and a vertical axis called the *y*-axis. The **origin** is where the axes meet.

An **ordered pair** is two numbers that describe a specific point on a coordinate plane. These numbers are called coordinates. Marking ordered pairs on a coordinate plane is called graphing or plotting.

Decimal fraction

Decimal fractions are fractions in which the denominator is 10, 100, or 1,000, etc. but are always written using decimal points. For example: $\frac{3}{10}$ can be written as 0.3 and $\frac{28}{100}$ can be written as 0.28.

A **decimal point** indicates which digit is in the ones place. It is positioned immediately to the right of the ones digit. For example, in the numeral 23.85, 3 is in the ones place.

A digit's **decimal place** is its position on the right-hand side of the decimal point. The first decimal place to the right of the decimal point is the tenths place. The next place is called hundredths. For example, in the numeral 23.85, 8 is in the first decimal place so it has a value of 8 tenths.

Expanded form

Expanded form is a method of writing numbers as the sum of the values of each digit. For example: $1.842 = (1 \times 1) + (8 \times \frac{1}{10}) + (4 \times \frac{1}{100}) + (2 \times \frac{1}{1000})$

Exponents

Exponents are often used to represent multi-digit numbers. Using exponents involves repeatedly multiplying a base number. The diagram shows that 10^3 is equivalent to $10 \times 10 \times 10$, so $10^3 = 1,000$.

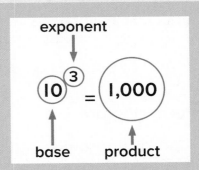

Factor

Factors are whole numbers that evenly divide another whole number. For example, 4 and 5 are both factors of 20 and 20 is a multiple of both 4 and 5.

Length

Customary Units of Length		Metric Units of Length	
12 inches (in)	1 foot (ft)	10 millimeters (mm)	1 centimeter (cm)
3 feet	1 yard (yd)	100 centimeters	1 meter (m)
1,760 yards	1 mile (mi)	1,000 meters	1 kilometer (km)

Line plot

A **line plot** is used to show data.
On this line plot, each dot represents one student.

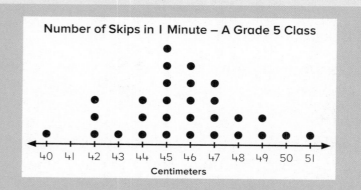

Mass (weight)

Customary Units of Mass		Metric Units of Mass	
16 ounces (oz)	1 pound (lb)	1,000 grams (g)	1 kilogram (kg)

Order of operations

If there is **one** type of operation in a sentence, work left to right.
If there is **more than one** type of operation, work left to right in this **order**:

1. Perform any operation inside parentheses.

2. Multiply or divide pairs of numbers.

3. Add or subtract pairs of numbers.

Parallelogram

A **parallelogram** is a quadrilateral with exactly two pairs of parallel sides.

Perimeter

A **perimeter** is the boundary of a shape and the total length of that boundary. For example, the perimeter of this rectangle is 20 inches.

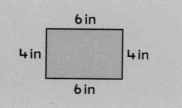

Triangle

A **scalene triangle** has no sides that are equal in length and no angles equal in size.

An **isosceles triangle** has at least two sides of equal length and at least two angles equal in size.

An **equilateral triangle** has three sides of equal length and three angles equal in size.

Volume

Volume is the amount of space that an object occupies. This amount is usually described in cubic units such as cubic centimeters (cm^3) or cubic inches (in^3).

TEACHER INDEX

© ORIGO Education